PRAISE for *Crisis Interr* *Residential Treatment for Ch*

M000236627

If you are experiencing this journey with your child or family member this book does an incredible job walking you through the process. From potential questions or concerns - everything is addressed. Each family needs to recount that you are not alone and deserve the attention and direction. Lucy has the experience, wherewith all, and expertise to work with all types of families and backgrounds.

Effie Goldberg
Managing Director
Ascend Healthcare

This desperately needed, extraordinarily helpful volume fills a necessary niche. Filled with the hard-won expertise of both professional and personal insight, Lucy will help you along your family's critical journey. Mixing homespun wisdom with clinical insight, this book will be a gift to parents and professionals alike.

David Altshuler, MS
Author of *Get Your Kid into the Right College.*
Get the Right College into your Kid

I had the good fortune to work with Lucy when my son was in crisis. I wish we had this book then. Lucy's writing is clear, concise and walks you through how the residential treatment world works. I recommend this book as a must-read for any parent who is considering residential treatment for their child or beginning to consider working with an educational consultant. It will be your bible!

Mara Glauberg
Randolph, NJ

This book is a must-read for any parent or professional supporting a child or young adult who is struggling to cope despite outpatient treatment and school-based support. Lucy's book reflects her years of experience with therapeutic placement for individuals with complex mental health, learning, neurodevelopmental, trauma, or addiction issues as well as her ability to communicate with clarity, wisdom, and compassion. "Crisis Interrupted" is a lifeline for parents and a needed resource for mental health, education, and medical professionals.

Jane Brown, Psy.D.
Licensed Psychologist

If you are considering residential treatment, whether your child is on the autism spectrum, is struggling with depression and anxiety or is making very poor decisions, you must read this book. Lucy concisely describes the process, offers hope and generously shares her expertise to parents who are facing incredibly hard decisions.

Carla Shorts, MS, LPC
Admissions Director
Black Mountain Academy

CRISIS
INTERRUPTED

A Parent's Guide to Residential Treatment for Children, Teens & Young Adults

LUCY PRITZKER

Crisis Interrupted: A Parent's Guide to Residential Treatment for Struggling Children, Teens and Young Adults

ISBN: 978-1-09830-077-7 (Paperback) eBook 978-1-09830-078-4

The names and identifying details of certain individuals have been changed to protect their privacy. Although I am a therapeutic and educational consultant, I am not your consultant. Reading this book does not create a consultant-client relationship between us. This book should not be used as a substitute for the advice of a professional.

Printed in the United States of America.
First printing edition February 2020.

Elm Street Placements
66 Elm Street #13
Westfield, NJ, 07090
www.ElmStreetPlacements.com

To the families who have allowed me to walk alongside them in their journeys and trusted me to be part of their healing; you are real life super-heroes.

To the professionals who fulfill my promise of hope to my clients; you are true healers.

And lastly, in memory of an outstanding educator and psychologist whose wise words have shaped the work I do with families and students more than anything else. You not only saved my family, but through my work you have saved countless others.

ACKNOWLEDGEMENTS

Thank you to my dear husband, David. Your belief I could get this written was my biggest driving force. Thank you for always believing in me.

To my three children, Abe, Hannah and Ben, thank you for your unending cheerleading while I wrote this book.

I'm immensely grateful to my mother. Thank you for your guidance and encouragement and inspiring me to do it all, just like you!

Sincerest thanks to my Elm Street Placements colleagues: Raegan for the calming voice our clients hear first; Sharon for your midnight lists that keep my brain organized; Kathy and Fran for always recognizing the seriousness of the work we do. Your compassion and expertise inspire me every day!

To Samme Chittum, my editor, I appreciate your patience, your knowledge, and your tolerance for my last-minute additions. To Bob Scott for being the brainchild of this book- you knew I had it in me before I did, thank you. And Dr. Jennifer Zeisz, for your chapter contribution and rolling with the flow.

Dear Reader,

I hope the process of finding your child a therapeutic program is made easier with this guide. Although there is a lot of information shared here, nothing can replace the expertise and guidance of an educational consultant.

Please reach out to my educational consulting firm, Elm Street Placements, and speak to a consultant in our office. If we are unable to help you, we will gladly refer you to someone who will be appropriate for your specific situation.

Lucy Pritzker

Elm Street Placements, Inc.

66 Elm Street #13

Westfield, New Jersey 07090

(908) 228-2212

Lucy@ElmStreetPlacements.com

www.ElmStreetPlacements.com

Contents

Peek into my office and you'll see desperate parents and hear tales of heartbreak. Stay a while and you'll understand why I love my work. I provide solutions. Not just hope, actual solutions.

I am an educational and therapeutic placement consultant, and I personally know hundreds of programs. One of them will change your child's life – and yours too.

In a typical month, I will visit eight to ten programs around the country. Some may be new to me and others I have been to many times. I make sure they are maintaining their high standards and often visit a student I have placed there. During that same month I will meet with parents, most of whom are concerned and some who are frantic. The frantic parents usually are those who are helplessly watching their child descend into drug addiction or mental illness. The concerned parents are those whose child needs a different learning environment, one that respects the unique needs of their child.

Parents find me through other parents whom I have worked with. Sometimes program staff will suggest working with me to make sure the family has guidance before enrolling. Most often, it is psychologists and psychiatrists who tell their patients about the service I provide.

I didn't always work helping families find the right placements for their children. But I have always worked with children and families. I began my career as a teacher, and found myself drawn to the student who was struggling in some way: the underdog being teased on the playground, the sixth grader who couldn't sound out first-grade words, the sad high schooler who confided in me about how difficult his home situation really was.

It was in my life as a parent that I got my real education in the residential treatment world. When my eldest was born, I assumed all babies required constant attention, that everyone locked up and triple baby-proofed their house and needed two adults to manage their child. I couldn't understand why other children easily separated from their mothers for playdates, soccer practice or piano lessons. When it came to my son, however, he became frantic if I even stepped into the shower and had a meltdown if the cream cheese showed through the hole in his bagel.

I've lived the trauma of hospitalizing a young child to keep him and the rest of the family safe. I watched as the psychiatrist threw medication after medication at my son – like darts flung at a dartboard – in the vain hope that something would stick. I know the utter panic of begging, pleading, bribing, threatening and ultimately dragging a child into school each day. And I know the gut-wrenching feeling of realizing that my boy couldn't live at home. Couldn't live in a family. I also know the absolute joy of seeing him get the right help in a residential program and even thrive there. He's an adult now, with a college degree, supporting himself in a field he has always loved. Of all my three children, he is the one who most loves spending time with family. He is a warm, caring young man who doesn't bear the scars of his early trauma. I know it is because we were so intentional about where we sought help and where he went to school.

My life was a painful, heartbreaking nightmare, and no one knew how to help me. I was in uncharted territory without a guide and had to blaze my own trail. But you don't have to. Guiding other families so they can see the light at the end of the tunnel, and ultimately out the other end, is why I do this. I have the privilege of helping families during the most difficult time of their lives, and the pleasure of being on their journey as their child and their family gets healthy again.

If you are reading this book, you are about to make one of the, if not *the*, most difficult parenting decisions you will ever have to make. The good news is you don't have to face it alone.

CHAPTER 1

Working with an Educational Consultant

Educational consultants, or ECs, are the link between families and private-pay therapeutic schools, therapeutic wilderness programs, residential treatment centers, and stabilization and assessment centers.

You might have been told that an educational consultant is someone who guides school administrators to best practices or someone who helps families through the college application process. Discovery Toys, a toy company, calls their salespeople "educational consultants." Apparently, I've dedicated my life to a career that is a misnomer.

More accurately, an educational consultant is the professional used by families with a struggling child to help them explore residential (and in some cases) day treatment options. An EC is the expert with first-hand knowledge of mental health treatment programs. Educational consultants are professional therapeutic placement specialists. "I had no idea there were people who do what you do, until today when I'm in desperate need," is a typical comment from a parent inquiring about my services. Parents are relieved to learn there is an expert who can guide them through this daunting process during such an overwhelming time. And, of course, the parents are also heartbroken to know they need the services of a consultant.

Who is an Educational Consultant?

Educational consultants come from varied backgrounds. Some have had previous careers as mental health professionals, some have worked as educators, special education advocates, and others come to the profession having had "on the job training" as a parent of a child who needed a therapeutic placement.

Educational consulting is not a licensed profession. There is no licensing board that oversees the work and provides standards that ECs perform. There are, however, voluntary associations to which ECs can belong. A leader in the field is the Independent Educational Consultant Association. The IECA requires its members to adhere to the highest professional standards. I recommend you consider working with an EC who has been accepted into the IECA. You'll be working with an expert who has a proven track record of professionalism and training. (FYI, full disclosure: I am a member of the IECA board of directors.)

In order to become a member, therapeutic IECA members must:

- Have an applicable master's degree or higher (or demonstrates comparable learning)
- Have a minimum of three years' experience in therapeutic placement
- Demonstrate a knowledge of test interpretation and processes for placement
- Have conducted a minimum of fifty evaluative visits
- Have worked with a minimum of thirty clients on admission and placement
- Have a peer review of their website and promotional materials for appropriateness of parental claims

What Do ECs Do?

ECs travel. We travel a lot! We spend time at all the programs we refer our clients to. We explore the campuses, looking in on classrooms and touring dorm rooms, dining halls and outdoor spaces. We spend time with administrators, therapists, teachers and, most importantly, the students. We assess the programs for their safety, their clinical expertise, and their academics. We understand who fits in socially in the program and who doesn't. We know what issues the program specializes in and where their expertise lies. When I give a family options for residential treatment, my suggestions are based on my first-hand knowledge of the programs.

ECs meet with parents. When I first began working in this field, I designed lots of paperwork. It seemed more professional to have parents fill out forms – an intake form, a mental health form, a family history form. Mr. and Mrs. Daniels dutifully filled out all ten pages I had emailed and brought them to our initial consultation. I asked questions, and they pointed to the place on the well-organized form where they had filled in the answers.

"When was the first time Alex refused to go to school?" I asked. "October of tenth grade," his mom said, and pointed to question number eight.

I got the answer, but I didn't get information. I really was curious about when Alex's school refusal began. However, more than wanting to know the information, I needed to know how this household operated and the stories around the scenario. So, over the years I have changed the structure of my meetings with parents.

In contrast, when the O'Learys came in, sans paperwork, I asked the same question and was able to gain far more insight into the family's dynamics and needs. "When did she start avoiding school?" Both parents paused, and then Mrs. O'Leary said, "It was the middle of her sophomore year."

"No," her husband interjected, correcting his wife. "Wasn't it when she had a stomach virus in the beginning of junior year?"

And then they discussed it. "It was just before we went on the cruise," Mrs. O'Leary said. "Remember how mad she was when we wouldn't let her stay home to pack because she was starting to miss too many days?"

"No! *You* were going to let her stay home, but I wouldn't let her," Mr. O'Leary quipped. Then he turned to me, adding, "My wife *always* gives in."

In my office now, forms are gone, parents don't have to do burdensome paperwork, and I get more useful information through listening, following my curiosity and witnessing interactions.

ECs read documents. Sometimes parents drop off file cabinets full of evaluations for me to review. Other times there isn't a lot of documentation to read through. I review psychological and educational testing and also school report cards. Grades help me understand how a child functions in school, but the teacher's comments can be even more telling. "Sarah does very well on in-class assignments, but fails to hand in assignments on time." "She is rarely prepared for class." "While her ideas are creative, Sarah struggles to begin projects and her follow through is lacking."

I read Sarah's report cards, her progress reports from her counselor-in-training job at camp and her neuropscyhological[1] evaluation her parents had done by a private psychologist.

I looked for common threads: "Sarah is a pleasure to have in class. I would love it if she spoke up more." "The children in Sarah's care at camp

---

1 An indepth discussion of neuropscyhological evaluations is included in a supplementary chapter at the end of the book.

loved her! It seemed it was challenging for her to ask her supervisor for time off for the family trip." "Sarah was cooperative during our two testing sessions. She was initially quiet and warmed up some, but was still noticeably guarded."

ECs meet with the child/teen. I explain to the child, as I did last week when working with Sarah, that although I am an expert on schools and programs, I am not an expert on Sarah. She is the true Sarah expert. What does she love to do? Interests and strengths are equally as important to my process as are the areas she is struggling in. And then, we discuss what she hates to do, what she dislikes, what scares her, etc.

Typically, meetings with students like Sarah last about an hour. Sometimes, however, the youngster can't tolerate more than a few minutes of time with me, while others may talk for hours on end.

Often parents are worried the child won't speak to me or will be rude. And yes, this happens. And it's fine. That's the information I am looking for. Words spoken aren't as important as our interaction, or lack thereof. In some cases, I don't meet the child. Occasionally, the treatment team, the parents, or I determine that it's not safe. For some children or teens, knowing that parents are making plans to send them to a residential program may provoke them to hurt themselves, hurt others, or run away.

Speaking with the Team

I speak with professionals who have worked with the child within the last few years. This may include babysitters, SAT tutors, as well as the traditional medical and psychological team members. Teachers, too, provide valuable information. Teachers tell me how the child reacts to unstructured time in the classroom, how the child handles classroom frustration and competition, and how the child is perceived by the other students.

Specialists are excellent at examining their particular area of expertise – *e.g.* medication, psychotherapy, academics, or recreation. It is the EC who pulls all the information together. I ask specialists and anyone else who has tried to help the child their impression of the care needed and their opinion about the diagnosis. I also ask every person I speak with which of their methods have worked with that child and which have not. Once I've gathered all of the information I need, I reach out to my contacts at the appropriate residential programs. These are professionals with whom I maintain a collegial relationship.

I speak to them about Sarah, her testing, the visit she and I had together, and what her teachers and treatment team said. I want to make sure the peer group is right. I'm not just referring to a program, but often a specific therapist.

Then it's time for me to present the parents with the short list of programs I have identified as being the best options for their child. I am available to the parents as they interview the optioned schools. I help them ask the right questions. Vetting each program is a process that is necessary and worthwhile. I encourage the parents to call or visit the programs, ask about things important to them, what issues the others in the group are there for, who the therapist will be, how often they will have the opportunity to speak to their child, and so on.

Sometimes, after all the work and all the back-and-forth discussions, parents are still hesitant. *Is it right to send my child away? Will my child never forgive me? Who will my child be exposed to in that environment?*

So, we talk some more. I tell them about other families who've done this; then I show them some correspondence, such as emails I've received – some from parents, some from the students. These graduates of therapeutic programs, and their parents, have eagerly consented, so that I may share excerpts from their letters and emails with hesitant families. (I've not used their last name nor the name of the program they were in.) Here are a few:

> *- Lucy, please convince other kids to go to A. It was the best, except the food wasn't always good. I have a happy life now, and it's all because I went there.*

> *- We were afraid to let go of Max and now we know it was the wisest decision. He's a new kid. I wouldn't believe it if I didn't see it! He even gets along with his brother and sister.*

> *- I left my anxiety at H. I went there with so many fears and phobias I could hardly breathe, but after I was there for a while, I couldn't remember what scared me or why those things bothered me so much. It was like magic.*

- I like school. Could you believe that? Remember when I came to your office and told you school was poison. I read books now, too. Novels, fiction.

- We've got our daughter back. I apologize for doubting you at first. You knew what we didn't know. That there was a place she would fit in and be accepted just the way she is. Thank you, thank you.

- You were the only one who figured out I didn't want to do all those things I was doing. I hated when you said the only way to stop was to get away from my friends. Remember that time in your office when I was begging my parents to move? I'm glad they didn't listen to me.

And the decision is made, the school or program is chosen, admission is scheduled and the entire family changes – for the better.

When Is the Right Time to Hire an EC?

Now that you are familiar with educational consultants, how do you know when you and your child need one? I recommend considering a consultation with an EC if more than one of these situations below pertains to you:

- You've tried outpatient therapy with no or minimal results
- You've tried medication with no or minimal results
- Your child has been hospitalized and symptoms persist
- Consequences for your child's actions don't result in change
- Alternative schools, such as home schooling, aren't working
- You are walking on eggshells around your child to avoid conflict and meltdowns
- Police have been involved
- You jump every time the phone rings, thinking it's the school or camp etc., telling you about a crisis with your child
- Family life is disrupted because of child's behavior
- Your child is refusing to go to school
- Your child is refusing to leave the bedroom for meals
- Your attempts at setting limits result in physical outbursts from your child

- Your child's behavior is frightening or bizarre
- Your child talks about hating herself and hating life
- Your child's daily functioning is impaired by alcohol or other drugs
- Therapists/teachers/doctors have no answers, or their answers aren't helpful
- Therapists/teachers/doctors are blaming your parenting

If your child is currently in crisis, whether at home, in a hospital, or even in jail, call an educational consultant now. Researching programs on your own can yield information, but there are a large number of programs, and they all have enticing websites. You'll do best if you rely on expert advice because the options are overwhelming – many, many programs promise they can help you. Many are excellent for the right child but can be awful for the wrong one. An EC will know if your child is the right fit. Working with an EC means you will get the placement right the first time and save you and your family lots of heartache and tens of thousands of dollars.

Whom Do ECs Help?

In my office, we place children as young as five or six, tweens, teens and young adults usually under thirty, although the age bracket for "young adult" is increasing each year.

The majority of children, teens and young adults whom I see have been diagnosed with one or more of the following: a psychiatric condition, mental disorder, developmental disorder or learning disorder. Some clients don't have a diagnosis, either because they haven't been to a specialist who can diagnose them, or they don't meet the criteria for a diagnosis, but are still struggling and require some sort of intervention. Typical diagnoses and concerns that ECs work include the following:

- Attention deficit hyperactivity disorder (ADHD)
- Specific learning disabilities
- Autism spectrum disorder
- Nonverbal learning disability
- Executive functioning issues
- Anxiety

- Obsessive Compulsive Disorder (OCD)
- Depression
- Bipolar disorders
- Personality disorders or emerging personality disorders
- Substance abuse
- Adoption[2]
- Attachment disorders
- Trauma
- Anger issues
- Failure to launch
- LGBTQ issues[3]
- Eating disorders

How Do You Choose an EC?

Here are some questions you might want to ask when you interview an EC. And yes, you should interview, especially if you don't know anyone else who has used this person's services.

*Ask if the EC visits programs. You want someone who knows the place your child will be living or receiving treatment; you don't want someone who relies upon websites and phone calls to learn about the program.

*Ask if the EC works alone or has employees. You want to know about the experience and qualifications of any other consultants in the practice with whom you may be interacting. Also, ask if there is an administrative assistant in the office to accept calls or mailings.

*Ask if the EC is available while on the road. Determine if and how you will reach your consultant when they are traveling and visiting programs.

---

2 A child who has been adopted may experience difficulties related to their adoption. If difficulties do arise, the child or teen sometimes needs the additional support provided by skilled professionals.
3 A child, teen or young adult who identifies as gay or transgender may at some point need the additional support of skilled professionals to help them navigate a range of social, emotional and identity-based challenges.

*Ask for the names of professional organizations to which the EC belongs. You want some reassurance that there are known standards adhered to by the EC.

*Ask if the EC specializes in particular issues, such as learning disabilities, drug addiction, bipolar disorder, autism spectrum disorder, twice exceptional students, suicidal behavior . . . the list goes on and on.

*Ask how long this person has worked as a consultant. This is not a rude question. It's important to know if the EC is new to the profession, because then you'll want to know that there is some supervision available to him or her.

*Ask about the EC's involvement after the placement is made. Will the EC be talking to you, to your child, to someone at the program, throughout the placement?

*Ask if the EC gets paid by the program – a referral fee. The IECA forbids this. The organization believes that your educational consultant should be working for you and only for you. Referral fees may encourage placement that doesn't keep your child's best interests at the forefront.

*Ask if the EC will meet you and your child in person. Or do they prefer doing everything via phone/Facetime/video conferencing, etc.

*Ask about a contract. An explicit contract is necessary.

*Ask about the fee you will pay your educational consultant. Know what is covered by that fee and what is not.

*Ask about the training and educational background of the EC.

A consultant's role isn't just to give you a list of appropriate programs. They are now part of your family's journey and will be with you before, during and after the treatment program. So choose wisely! Make sure your EC is someone you feel comfortable with and someone you trust.

CHAPTER 2

Outpatient Mental Health

You may already have consulted the usual mental health and academic professionals. When a child is having difficulty with his or her emotional regulation and with being a positive family member or student, it is time for an intervention. Sometimes, the pediatrician is consulted. Sometimes the child's teacher is consulted. A doctor will explore a physical cause for these symptoms. The doctor may perform a blood test and other medical tests and exams. If these return normal results, a psychotherapist is frequently the next stop. Similarly, a teacher may recommend your child see a therapist to help your child manage his emotions.

Typically, this means outpatient, individual psychotherapy. Psychotherapy can be administered by a psychologist, a psychiatrist, a social worker, or a mental health counselor.

A _psychologist_ may have a Ph.D. in education, psychology, or counseling; or he or she may have a Psy.D. degree. A psychology license permits the practitioner to evaluate, diagnose and conduct therapy in groups or individual sessions.

A _psychiatrist_ is a medical doctor who received an MD degree from medical school, did an internship and then a residency in general psychiatry. I recommend that my clients see only a board-certified child and adolescent psychiatrist. That is a psychiatrist who has had two additional years of training in dealing with situations unique to children and teenagers.

Psychiatrists can evaluate, diagnose, conduct therapy and can prescribe medication. Often, psychiatrists only provide medication management. That means that after diagnosing, prescribing, and stabilizing the patient on a medication, they will refer the patient to a therapist for psychotherapy and see the patient less frequently.

A _social worker_ may be trained in mental health counseling, or community organizing and advocacy. A clinical social worker will have an MSW degree or a DSW degree; he or she may also be trained to be a psychotherapist. Many clinical social workers go to advanced institutes of psychotherapy training and become licensed LCSW therapists.

There are psychotherapists and counselors who are master's level clinicians trained in mental health issues, sometimes in specific modalities, such as cognitive behavioral therapy (CBT), behavioral therapy, dialectical behavioral therapy (DBT), psychodynamic therapy, and more. Therapists usually see their patient once a week for about 45 minutes to an hour. Sometimes a second weekly session may be recommended. During the session they will discuss the patient's symptoms and formulate coping skills and strategies. Therapists usually hold state licenses in their area of expertise.

For some children and teens, once or twice a week therapy isn't enough. Their mental health symptoms – sadness, anxiety, anger, and more – continue to interfere with their daily living, with their school life and with their home life. These individuals need the support of their therapist more often. Their maladaptive behaviors – avoidance, substance use, eating issues, lashing out – prevent them from functioning at a healthy level. This is when the educational consultant steps in to find the best program for your child.

Outpatient Program Options

Sometimes an educational consultant may recommend that your child remain at home but attend a different school. ECs are familiar with therapeutic day schools and can explain why they may or may not be the best option for your child. Also, some mental health issues can be treated while living at home and attending an intensive outpatient program or a partial hospitalization program. Here are their descriptions:

Intensive Outpatient Program:

IOPs are sometimes run through psychiatric hospitals (also called behavioral health hospitals), and sometimes are private programs that are unaffiliated with a hospital. IOPs typically run two to three hours a day, three to five days a week. Patients meet with their individual therapist once a week and attend group therapy the rest of the time. Consultation with a psychiatrist to discuss medication may or may not be available. In the past, IOPs were used for substance abuse treatment, however it is now a model that is being used more and more for other mental health issues.

Partial Hospitalization Program:

If your child's functioning deteriorates to the point that he or she is no longer attending school and his or her symptoms are not stable, you may be directed to a PHP or partial hospitalization program. PHP patients attend this program in the place of going to school, five days a week, five to seven hours a day. They attend group therapy, recreation therapy and individual therapy. There is a psychiatrist at the facility to meet with patients about medication. Sometimes PHP is used after someone discharges from an inpatient stay at a psychiatric hospital.

Therapeutic Day Schools:

Therapeutic day schools are an alternative when mental health symptoms prevent a student from attending traditional schools. In addition to a full academic curriculum, these schools provide individual and group therapy, and sometimes family therapy and psychiatry. Such schools may cater to particular student profiles, including students with learning disabilities, gifted students, aggressive behaviors, autism spectrum, substance abuse, etc. Classes in art, physical education, as well as clubs and sports are typically offered. Many of these schools have policies limiting student use of electronics during the day.

Wrap Around Care:

For families where both parents work, or even when one parent stays at home but there are siblings or other demands on a caregiver's attention; after school and weekends can be especially problematic times for a child struggling with mental health issues. Wrap around care provides therapeutic childcare after school, and sometimes student mentoring to encourage activities in home and the community.

Care provided on an outpatient basis is not one-size fits all. More than one option is available. Outpatient treatment typically progresses along an established continuum of care, as seen in the following diagram.

The Outpatient Continuum

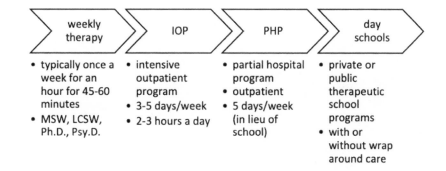

weekly therapy	IOP	PHP	day schools
• typically once a week for an hour for 45-60 minutes • MSW, LCSW, Ph.D., Psy.D.	• intensive outpatient program • 3-5 days/week • 2-3 hours a day	• partial hospital program • outpatient • 5 days/week (in lieu of school)	• private or public therapeutic school programs • with or without wrap around care

Outpatient Continuum

Outpatient Therapy

- LCSW or Masters level therapist or psychologist (Ph.D. or Psy.D.)
- typically forty-five minutes to one-hour sessions
- once a week

Intensive Outpatient

- in a psychiatric hospital or free-standing building
- three to five days per week
- weekly individual therapy
- daily group therapy
- psychiatry may or may not be available

Partial Hospital Program

- instead of going to school
- five days a week
- five to seven hours a day
- weekly individual therapy
- daily group and recreation therapy
- psychiatry typically available

Therapeutic Day School

- mental health symptoms prevent student from attending traditional school
- individual and group therapy
- full academic day
- often specific to particular student profiles: learning disabilities, gifted students, aggressive behaviors, autism spectrum, substance abuse, etc.
- art, physical education, clubs, sports

Wrap Around Care

- after-school and weekend support
- in home or in community, or both
- private pay or insurance

A Case Study: Liam

I'd like you to meet Liam. Liam is a thirteen-year-old boy whose therapeutic journey involved outpatient care that ultimately included transitioning to a partial hospital program. Liam's depressive symptoms began at age eleven, "pretty gradually," his mother remarked. "We noticed in early spring of fifth grade he stopped being interested in playing baseball after school with his friends like he'd been doing for the entire school year. He filled the time with video games. And when we put restrictions and time limits on his games, he became really angry." After talking with Liam's school counselor, the parents were directed to see Dr. Irling, a psychologist who specializes in children and adolescents. Liam met, reluctantly, with Dr. Irling a few times for an assessment, which included talking with Liam and taking a history from the parents. Dr. Irling diagnosed Liam with depression. Liam saw Dr. Irling in his office once a week for the remainder of the school year. There was concern that Liam's depression might worsen over the summer when he didn't have his usual school year routine, which gave him necessary structure, so Dr Irling referred them to a psychiatrist who put Liam on an antidepressant medication.

Liam started the next school year strongly, getting good grades and spending time with his friends again. However, by late October he was again starting to feel overwhelmed at school. He argued with his sister a lot, slammed doors, cursed at his parents and was beginning to fall behind with school assignments. At a therapy session with Dr. Irling, Liam said that he wished he could just disappear. Liam's parents were hearing similar thoughts at home. "It was both scary and heartbreaking to hear my thirteen-year-old say we would be better off without him," said his dad. Dr. Irling recommended Liam attend an IOP program. He did, but instead of getting better, Liam was struggling to get out of bed in the mornings and would resist his parents' attempts at limiting his electronics. "He was playing video games all night long and sleeping during the day. We walked on eggshells not to set him off. His anger scared us, and maybe scared him, too. He was out of control when angry. But, worse than his anger towards us and his sister, was the sadness he had about how bad things had become," his dad recounted. Liam's therapeutic team recommended Liam take time off from school and enroll in a PHP program where he would get more hours of therapy and have a psychiatrist available to monitor medication changes.

"When I look back on how things had changed in just a year, I can't believe it. We used to have to drag him home from the baseball field, and now we spend our days wishing he would go outside, and dragging him from therapy appointment to therapy appointment," Liam's mom told me.

Over the course of six weeks, Liam started showing signs of his "old-self" again. He smiled more, he stopped playing video games as much and started seeing his baseball friends again. After a two-month hiatus, Liam returned to his regular school and was able to cope much better. The PHP program worked. He still saw Dr. Irling each week and had his medications monitored by the psychiatrist every few months.

CHAPTER 3

Residential Treatment Options

So what do you do if outpatient therapy doesn't work? When your child isn't Liam? What if your child doesn't get better after PHP? You've had your child in individual, family, and group therapy, maybe even an intensive outpatient program or partial hospitalization. And at some point, you realize, all the outpatient therapy in the world isn't the answer. You see your child's behaviors and symptoms regressing right back to where they were, or worse.

If you are reading this book, chances are this is your situation. Not everyone is a Liam, but everyone can be helped. Join me in exploring higher levels of care beyond outpatient treatment. Together we will find just what your child and your family need.

If your EC believes your child needs another option because all outpatient therapy has failed and a new school is not the answer, it's time to look for the appropriate residential placement. Your EC will tell you which type of placement will be most helpful to your child. Just like the continuum of care of outpatient mental health options, which start with the pediatrician and go all the way through to partial hospitalization, there is a continuum of care of residential options.

Acute Inpatient Psychiatric Hospitalization

When a child is a danger to him or herself or to someone else, an inpatient psychiatric hospitalization may be recommended. The child usually enters this mental health system via ambulance and is taken to a hospital emergency room by parents or police.

Proactive Tips

Many communities have crisis intervention hotlines that are appropriate to call if your child is having a crisis and you don't know if you need to go to the hospital or not. They will come to your home and deescalate and assess the situation. Find out their phone number before you need them.

Visit your local police department to let them know your address. Explain that they may get dispatched to that address because you have a child with mental illness. (Your child may or may not have this label, but it is language police understand.) Discuss ways of interacting and communicating that help calm your child. It's also a good idea to let them know what to expect when they arrive. (Will she lash out verbally at them? Hide under the bed?) This conversation will help ensure that the police approach your out-of-control child in a calm, compassionate way should you need them to come to your home.

Acute psychiatric hospitals (sometimes referred to as behavioral health hospitals) can be part of a larger medical hospital or a standalone facility. The treatment and length of stay in these facilities are almost always dictated by insurance. Thus, someone from the insurance company, who has never met your child, determines what will happen during the hospital stay and for how long.

Your child is placed in an acute, inpatient hospital or unit for safety reasons – he or she needs the containment of a psychiatric facility. The typical length of stay, mandated by the insurance company, is three to five days. Sometimes insurance companies allow the patient to stay longer, but more than two weeks is practically unheard of these days. There was a time when psychiatric hospitals would keep an unruly teen for months to make sure medication and behaviors were in check before they issued a discharge. Those days are gone.

During this short-term hospital stay, there is a focus on medication and usually some therapy groups are available. Unlike medical hospital stays, psychiatric hospitals do not allow parents to stay with their children and visiting hours are strictly limited, often an hour or two a few days a week. Although a child may have an outpatient psychiatrist, psychiatric hospitals do not grant privileges to outpatient doctors the way a medical hospital does. Your outpatient team may or may not be consulted about your child's medications and treatment plan.

Once the hospital team determines the patient is safe to leave, they should be discharging your child with a safety plan: what to do in case he or she again becomes a danger to him or herself or others, appointments within a few days to meet with a psychiatrist and therapist, and a plan to return to school. If it is determined that there is a need for more support, an IOP or PHP may be recommended.

In my consulting practice I see many children and teens who have been hospitalized but do not get sustainable relief from their symptoms, even after multiple admissions. It's not uncommon for a consultant to meet with parents while their child is in the hospital and move them to a residential program from there. Often this is a two-step process. The first being a two-to-three-month program designed to further assess, stabilize and treat before moving on to a longer-term residential program. Chapters four and five take a deep dive into first-step options. Chapters six, seven, eight and nine delve into longer residential options that often are a second step in the process.

The Residential Continuum

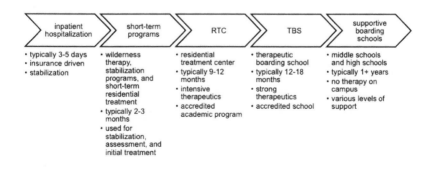

inpatient hospitalization	short-term programs	RTC	TBS	supportive boarding schools
• typically 3-5 days • insurance driven • stabilization	• wilderness therapy, stabilization programs, and short-term residential treatment • typically 2-3 months • used for stabilization, assessment, and initial treatment	• residential treatment center • typically 9-12 months • intensive therapeutics • accredited academic program	• therapeutic boarding school • typically 12-18 months • strong therapeutics • accredited school	• middle schools and high schools • typically 1+ years • no therapy on campus • various levels of support

CHAPTER 4

Therapeutic Wilderness and Outdoor Programs

I'd like you to meet Jason, age fifteen, who got the help he needed in a timely manner, thanks to a wilderness program. His mother is a single parent who was worried about her son's failing grades and dark moods. Here's what she told me.

A Case Study: Jason

"When I found out about my ex-husband's drug use and girlfriend, I packed up what I could and left with my two kids. Everything they had known and loved was gone. My daughter was pretty young and seemed to take it better than Jason. He was seven and missed his best friend and his dad and the dog. We moved across the country so I could be near family, but it also meant that visiting the only home he knew was out of the question."

Jason's dad wasn't involved with Jason or his sister for many years. Eventually, Jason's father stopped using drugs and got a steady job. He moved closer to his children and tried to be involved with them again. As his mother explained, "Jason had just started high school. Although he told me he was fine, I knew it was bringing up all kinds of stuff for him. Especially because his dad wasn't really good at sticking to the visiting schedule or doing what he promised."

Jason started missing school because of stomachaches. His mom took him to doctors who couldn't find any physical reasons for his pain. He started falling further and further behind with his schoolwork. "It just feels like a big mess," Jason told me. "My stomach hurts, my teachers are mad, my mom is mad. I guess my dad is mad. And I have so much work to do. I don't even understand most of it because I missed so many classes. I just feel like I can't go back now. I don't feel like I can do anything really at this point." He'd stopped seeing his friends, stopped going to his therapy appointments and spent most of his time under his covers in the darkness of his bedroom.

Jason needed a jumpstart to get him out of the house. He needed to rebuild his confidence, learn to deal with his chronic stomach pain and do work around his earlier losses and family relationships. I provided Jason's mom with a list of therapeutic wilderness programs for boys with similar issues. That list included very specific information about the therapist I wanted Jason to work with — someone who was skilled with teens who have had early losses and anxiety.

As counterintuitive as it may sound, having a young person engage in a program *outdoors,* without the walls of an office or a hospital, can be profound. Relying on tarps, sticks and dirt instead of walls, desks and chairs is often the answer for children and teens who have not progressed with traditional therapy.

Wilderness programs take place in remote locations and require participants to live primitively. At the same time, students engage in a therapeutic curriculum designed to get them back on track. In a wilderness program your child is fully involved in outdoor activities, including hiking, camping, backpacking and fire building. In addition, each adolescent has therapeutic assignments designed to teach coping skills, improve communication, rebuild damaged relationships and promote well-being. Personalized guidance is provided by a mental health professional who understands your child's challenges; the goal is to complete a therapeutic process and then identify future needs and interventions. This usually takes two-to-three months. ECs visit and evaluate wilderness programs for safety and staff excellence. Your consultant will know which program will best assess and then stabilize your child and treat his or her mental health issues. I have been in the woods countless times visiting students, field staff and therapists. I have traveled to assess programs in North Carolina, Colorado, Montana, Utah, Hawaii and beyond. Please be sure your EC has this experience, too.

Families often come to me with an erroneous, preconceived notion of what a therapeutic wilderness program is. "Bootcamp," "tear them down and build them back up," "deprivation," are amongst the false assumptions about wilderness programs. In reality, the wilderness programs that I use provide clinically sophisticated, gentle, compassionate environments that are neither punitive nor mean-spirited.

Some of my clients do go to wilderness programs for problems with drugs and alcohol; many other clients I carefully place in wilderness programs explicitly meant for "softer" issues, e.g., anxiety, poor self-esteem, impulsivity, social skills, etc. There are specific wilderness programs for young people on the autism spectrum, programs for kids who were adopted, and other wilderness programs for children and teens with OCD.

Unless your child is actively psychotic[4] there is a wilderness program – and even more specifically, a wilderness therapist – with expertise in just the areas in which your child struggles. The therapeutic wilderness experience frequently produces profound change.

Parents ask me, "Is wilderness safe?" According to the Outdoor Behavioral Health Council, or OBHC, therapeutic wilderness programs average injury rates are 1.12 per 1,000 participant days compared with backpacking: 2.05, downhill skiing: 3.28 and football practice: 19.74. While no treatment program can guarantee the total safety of any child, adolescents participating in OBHC programs are actually at less risk than adolescents not participating in these programs.[5]

Parents often ask me, "I know talking about your feelings can help, but I know my kid. He won't talk, so this is not an option. And anyway, how does hiking around and sleeping outside help?" I then go on to explain exactly why wilderness is so effective:

1.**Intervention**: Simply interrupting a teen's daily routine is very powerful. It sends a message to the teen that things must change and what is going on will no longer be tolerated.

2. **Unplugged**: Teens no longer have the distractions of cell phones, social media, video games, television, etc. And it's not just about electronics; it's about unplugging from distractions such as friends, family, and school, too. It's a chunk of time set aside to focus solely on themselves.

3. **No manipulation**: Manipulation and other maladaptive behaviors don't work in the wilderness. If it rains, all the begging, yelling, running away, and threatening won't

---

4 When someone has trouble understanding if their thoughts are real or not. Sometimes he or she will hear, see or believe things that aren't really there.
5 Michael Gass, H.L. Gillis, Keith C. Russel. Adventure Therapy: Theories, Research, and Practice. (New York: Routledge Press, 2010)

keep you dry; relying on others, following directions, and focusing on your own abilities to build shelter, will.

4. **Peer Group**: Something magical happens when you belong to a group that shares a language that outsiders don't understand. The jargon of wilderness programs is unique; just ask any kid who carried his P-food in his pack and busted a coal. (P-food is the abbreviation used in wilderness to delineate a participant's "personal" food from the group food. Busting a coal refers to igniting a small spark by rubbing two sticks together.)

Sharing a heartfelt letter from your parents with seven other teens out in the woods helps bond the members of the group together. A feeling of "we are all in this together" in a wilderness program creates a positive peer culture where helpfulness and honesty are valued.

5. **Experiential Learning:** By the time a teen gets to wilderness, he or she has most likely been through other types of therapies that haven't worked. But learning by doing does work. Success is its own reward.

6. **Nature Deficit Disorder**: There's something to be said about being out-of-doors. According to Richard Louv, author of the nonfiction book, *The Nature Principle*, reconnecting with the natural world is fundamental to our physical and mental health.

7. **Measurable Success**: Teens have measurable goals they need to accomplish in wilderness programs. To move up in a phase or level, they must demonstrate mastery of certain skills. For a struggling teen, having clearly delineated goals and immediate positive feedback works wonders.

8. **Power in Struggling**: Hard work builds character. Carrying a heavy pack, hiking an extra mile, or admitting a wrong are all helpful. Accomplishing the seemingly impossible feels awesome.

9. **Never Give Up**: If Johnny threatens his teacher when he feels frustrated, he very well may find himself expelled

from school. Johnny no longer has to face the frustration and learn a better way to cope. In wilderness there is no giving up. Persistence wins every time. The tables are turned in wilderness. Teens face frustration moment-to-moment as they navigate their new primitive lifestyle. Old patterns of handling frustration are anticipated by the staff. Cursing at a staff member doesn't land you a ticket home. Rather, during a teachable moment, the situation is processed, and new behaviors are suggested. Old patterns are slowly replaced with new, more appropriate coping strategies.

Remember Jason? His mom chose a wilderness program in Utah from the list I provided. Jason was ensconced in the high desert for ten weeks. At first, he struggled. He wanted to go back home to the comfort of his room. But with the support of his therapist, the field staff in the program and the guys in his group, Jason built resilience. He became able to talk about his feelings instead of withdrawing inward. He hiked. He cooked over a fire he and his group mates built from materials they gathered during the day. He wrote letters to his mother about how isolated he had been feeling, about how mad he was that his dad was unreliable, and how sad it made him to see his mom work so hard all day while he couldn't help and just lay in bed. And, he wrote about his stomach – it didn't hurt anymore!

What to Expect When Your Child Goes to a Wilderness Program:

Unlike getting ready for sleep-away camp, packing for wilderness is easy. The program supplies everything from underwear and bras, to sleeping bags and sunscreen. When your child is in a mental health crisis there is no time to buy gear, no time to go shopping.

You will have weekly phone calls with your child's therapist to get an update on his or her progress and to discuss work for you to do while your child is in the woods. Often this work entails reading pertinent books, writing letters that address specific concerns, and discussing possible scenarios. Because wilderness therapy is designed to limit distractions during a child's experience, families only visit once, occasionally twice, during the program. If appropriate, some programs have a therapeutic family visit midway. This takes place in the woods with wilderness staff who conduct therapeutic sessions to do face-to-face family therapy between the teen and parents and sometimes siblings.

The main communication between parents and their child in wilderness is through letter writing. Some parent letters are social: how the dog is getting along, what they did when Aunt Sally came for a visit. And other letters are therapeutic assignments from the therapist. For example, your child's therapist may ask you to write a letter that details the impact of your child's behavior on you and the rest of the family. Often this letter is read aloud to the group and processed with peers and staff. Throughout the wilderness experience, participants are taught how to give appropriate feedback that is useful to their peers' therapeutic journey.

Not only do you write to your child, your child will write to you. Each week you will receive a letter. Most letters home reflect the feelings of your child according to predictable stages of the therapeutic process. Expect a "rescue me" letter the first week:

Dear Mom and Dad,

This place is not what you thought it was. No one here gets better. One of the kids here was arrested twice and most of the other kids are drug addicts. Please get me out of here. I'll only get worse here. I promise I'll go to my therapy appointments. I'll even go every day if you take me home.

PS – The food is disgusting. I haven't eaten in two days. Seriously. Also, I have so many bug bites, I'm probably going to get malaria.

Love, John.

The next letter is usually one of resignation:

Dear Mom and Dad,

My therapist here told me that when he called you, you said there's no way I can come home yet. I don't understand why you would do this to me. I would rather be home, but I guess you are just going to leave me here to rot.

Love, John.

Then comes the good news:

Dear Mom and Dad,

You probably won't believe this, but I actually like it here!
We did this amazing hike. It took all day, but wow did I
feel great after. And the view! I wish you could have seen
it! I actually think this was a good idea that you made
me come here. I'm really working hard. I think I could
come home soon.

Love, John

Followed by:

Dear Mom and Dad,

Guess what? I've never felt better in my life! I have so
many things to tell you and teach you! I know most kids
take months to finish and get better, but I'm ready. I can
do it! Please come get me – you won't believe the changes
I've made!

Love, John

And now the real work begins. You will be coached by the therapist
to validate your child's experience in wilderness *and* maintain firm boundaries. Which looks something like this: "*John, your last letter sounded great!*
We are so glad to hear that you're enjoying the hiking. We hear you saying
that you've worked hard and are ready to come home. However, we plan to
have you continue at the program until your therapist and we agree you're
ready to graduate. Love, Mom and Dad

Together with your EC, around the midpoint of your child's wilderness stay, you'll begin to explore aftercare options. Working closely with
the wilderness therapist, your EC will gather information, and then contact
the appropriate aftercare programs to ensure that they have all the supports your child needs. This is when I often find myself on a satellite phone
call to the middle of the woods – and on some occasions on a plane to
Utah, North Carolina, or Colorado – because I need to have a conversation
with the teen to discuss her interests, her needs and her wants for her next
placement. At this juncture, you should be prepared for your next letter
from your child: The Wilderness High.

Dear Mom and Dad,

*This was the most successful ten weeks I have ever had. I
don't remember ever feeling this good. Thank you, thank
you. Love, John.*

After many weeks of fresh air, exercise, healthful food, excellent therapy and empowering activities, John feels terrific. Wilderness professionals call this a "wilderness high." Now that the real world beckons, some caution is necessary. Suddenly there are choices to make all day long – what to eat, what to wear, who to hang out with and what to do. There's also lots of noise, many more people to interact with and a very different structure to the day, or maybe very little structure. And that's why your EC will have already begun careful post-wilderness planning.

Although incredibly impactful, wilderness isn't designed for sustainable change. Think of it as learning to swim: In wilderness, it is as if your child has a swimming teacher next to him in the pool and he's wearing a life jacket, too. Returning home after the two-to-three-month experience in wilderness would be like throwing him into the deep end of the pool without an instructor and without a floatation device. He must first move to the middle of the pool with a lifeguard nearby.

Your EC, in consultation with you and the wilderness therapist, will recommend the appropriate next step. For some, the next step is a therapeutic boarding school, a residential treatment center, or perhaps a supportive boarding school. And sometimes, but not usually, the plan is to return home with many helpful services lined up.

A Case Study: Simon

Simon is sixteen and a student in eleventh grade. He was a high achiever in middle school and continued performing well in ninth grade. He joined the track team and had a nice friend group. Over the summer between ninth and tenth grades, Simon's grandmother became ill and his mom was preoccupied with her. Simon's grandmother eventually passed away while he was in tenth grade. Simon was very close to his grandmother. He took her death hard. His grades slipped, but he did seem to be putting in effort, and his grades weren't really *that* bad. Simon stopped running track. He started going to parties on the weekend, but no more than what his mom and dad had heard that other kids did. After a long week of lots of fighting with him, Simon's mom found marijuana in his laundry. She also noticed that his friend group had changed, and his grades had dropped. Simon's pediatrician suggested he see a therapist. The therapist concluded that Simon had ADHD in addition to grief issues surrounding his grandmother's death. Simon's pediatrician prescribed ADHD medication. It didn't seem to be effective, and a few weeks later his parents learned Simon was not taking his medication, but had instead been selling it. A big blow up ensued. Simon refused to go back to his therapist, who referred the parents to me. After careful consideration, information gathering and brainstorming, the decision was made to send Simon to a wilderness program for boys his age who were underachieving in school, using marijuana to relieve sadness (also called "self-medicating") and who had some recent losses in their lives. After ten weeks living outdoors and participating in the therapeutic wilderness experience, Simon was able to express his grief surrounding his grandmother's death and how it led him to numb his feelings, leading him to turn to marijuana. He took accountability for his lack of effort in school and for the way he treated his family. Simon committed to not using substances for twelve months while he continued his treatment at a therapeutic boarding school.

CHAPTER 5

Short Term Stabilization and Assessment Programs

There are some instances where wilderness programs aren't the best choice for a struggling child or teen. Your EC may suggest an indoor program instead of wilderness if there are medical issues to consider, such as type 1 diabetes. An indoor program may be preferable if there is a concern about psychosis. One alternative to wilderness is a stabilization and assessment program.

These programs can be housed in a psychiatric hospital, on their own campus with many buildings or in a home-like atmosphere where therapy appointments, meals and bedrooms are under one roof. The purpose of stabilization and assessment is just that. To bring a teen's mood and behavior to a workable level so he or she can enter longer term treatment ready to engage therapeutically, socially and academically. Parallel to the stabilization work, these programs assess their patients through a variety of methods:

- Observation
- Psychological testing
- Educational testing
- Medical testing
- Other assessments based on individual need

Families are involved in their child's program through family therapy typically conducted via phone or video, in-person visits and social phone calls. Some programs ask parents and the child to write letters to one another in addition to phone calls.

Your child's treatment team will assess your child's mental health throughout his or her stay and will assign a diagnosis (or diagnoses) to your child based on the observations and testing they have done. They will also explain the level of care your child needs and describe the criteria your EC should take into account when looking at aftercare.

When do kids go to short term assessment and stabilization programs?

- If there is a question as to what your child's diagnosis is
- If she was asked to leave a residential program
- If he cannot be served by a wilderness program
- If your child isn't stable enough to engage in longer term treatment but doesn't need an inpatient hospital stay.
- If the treatment team is not certain what the best course of treatment is

A Case Study: Cam

Cam's behavior was getting worse and worse at home. His difficulties weren't anything new; he had received early intervention when he was a toddler because he wasn't talking as much as other kids in his daycare. His public school had him on an individualized education plan (IEP) to help support him academically and during lunchtime when he felt overwhelmed. Cam met with a tutor after school for difficulties with math and science. Once a week he went to a therapist's office for individual therapy and another day he went to a social skills group there.

But Cam was still doing poorly in his classes. He had spent many days a week at the nurse's office during lunch; some days he would refuse to go to classes after lunch period was over and would stay at the nurse's office for the rest of the day. "He was a wreck at home," his mother told me. "Getting him up in the morning was so bad that I would go to bed dreading waking up in the morning and so happy when the weekends came, and we didn't go through that torture. He was increasingly mean to his twin sister, to the point that she avoided being home and is now staying with her grandparents. I think Cam may have taken money out of my purse last week. I was missing close to two hundred dollars and my husband noticed Cam had a new, expensive watch that he said a friend gave him. When we sat down to dinner and we didn't have ketchup, he went nuts. He threw his plate, ran upstairs and punched a hole in the wall."

Cam's therapist said he had a classic case of ADHD. His psychiatrist wasn't sure it was that clear. "With his social issues, and early speech delay, this may be autism spectrum disorder," she said. To further cloud the picture, Cam's tutor remarked more than once that Cam's anxiety really seemed to get in the way of him getting his work done. "It doesn't feel safe to keep him at home for much longer," his mother told me. "And the psychiatrist says he isn't a danger to himself or anyone else, so a hospital won't keep him."

Muddying the water even further, Cam had recently undergone knee surgery, and wasn't able to participate in hiking, so wilderness wasn't an option. After listening to Cam's history and understanding the family's goals, it was clear to me that he needed a very thorough assessment to determine what his diagnosis was and to prescribe treatment. If he was on the autism spectrum, he would need a specific type of residential setting. And if his difficulty came from his struggles with ADHD, an autism spectrum disorder program would be inappropriate. Cam was also on a lot of medication: a stimulant to keep him focused, an SSRI for his anxiety, an antipsychotic to help him regulate his behavior, and sleeping medication because some of his medication made it difficult for him to sleep at night.

Cam spent three weeks in an assessment and stabilization program where they did extensive testing to determine the source of Cam's struggles. Autism spectrum disorder was ruled out. It was determined that Cam's attentional issues made it very difficult for him to complete school tasks. This in turn made him very anxious to the point that he started avoiding his assignments, because he knew he ultimately wasn't going to be able to complete them. The testing also revealed Cam had difficulties processing language. This would require his team to understand students with learning styles like Cam and know how to tailor their lessons, both in and out of the classroom, to his specific needs. Cam's frustration and need for control stemmed from being misunderstood for a long time. Just like it took a long time to for Cam to be so out of control, it would take a long time for him to learn new skills to use in moments of inattention, frustration, anxiety, and feeling overwhelmed.

"The assessment was so helpful, and the results really made a lot of sense," Cam's mother later told me. "Cam started learning ways to manage his anxiety and behavior while he was there. And now in the program we selected with the help of our ed consultant, he is continuing that work. I think he feels really understood and feels hopeful again. Like he can be a good student and a nice kid."

CHAPTER 6

Residential Treatment Centers

Residential treatment centers or RTCs offer an intense immersion in mental health care. There is a full complement of individual, group and family therapy as well as some academic course work. When a student is placed in an RTC, a therapeutic staff member is supervising, watching, or interacting with that student at all times, even overnight. (In RTC lingo, this is known as "arms-length" or "line-of-site" supervision.) This means children are escorted everywhere they go: to the bathroom (with appropriate privacy,) to their therapist's office, to the basketball courts, etc.

The therapeutic team typically includes a psychiatrist who is available to you and your child's treatment team to make recommendations about medication. RTCs may be short term or long term. In short term residential care, treatment usually lasts thirty, sixty or ninety days. Long term RTCs, as the name implies, cover a longer period of time, typically nine months to a year or more.

When I was in graduate school in the early 1990s, my cohort of grad students were interns at "twenty-eight-day residential programs" for people with drug addiction. Why twenty-eight days? Really there was no reason. There is nothing in the research that shows that twenty-eight days is the magic number of days to produce the desired results. (As a matter of fact, current research shows that someone needs to be in treatment away from where they were using for a year to maintain their progress.) This was the amount of days insurance companies would pay. This has now changed into a thirty-day model, but sometimes it is extended to sixty or ninety days. It also now covers mental health without drug addiction and what is known as "dual diagnosis" – mental health and addiction occurring together. Twenty-eight, thirty, sixty or ninety days of treatment is arbitrary. The real goal should be to select a treatment program that is right for your child in all respects, including the length of time required to achieve long lasting results.

Short Term Residential Treatment Centers:

Unlike wilderness programs, these programs are indoors, and often in very posh surroundings, near the ocean, on estates, etc. In some cases, this may be an appropriate option. The day is spent in group therapy, and also individual and family therapy. Sometimes there is an academic component. Life skills, such as cooking, etc. may be offered. There may also be a wellness component with movement, nutrition and mindfulness. The cost can vary widely from completely covered by insurance to $75,000 per month and everything in between.

Typical Weekday Schedule at a Short Term RTC

7:00 a.m	Wake up
7:30 a.m.	Breakfast and medication
8:00 a.m	Daily intention group
8:30 a.m.	Yoga
9:30 a.m.	Shower and snack
10:15 a.m.	School
12:30 p.m.	Lunch and medication
1:30 p.m.	Group therapy
2:30 p.m	Snack
2:45 p.m.	Art therapy
4:00 p.m.	Homework, laundry and phone time
5:30 p.m	Dinner and cleanup
6:00 p.m.	Leisure and outdoor Recreation
7:00 p.m.	Process group
8:00 p.m.	Journaling
9:00 p.m.	Medication
9:30 p.m.	Daily review and meditation
10:30 p.m.	Lights out

Long Term Residential Treatment Centers

A word of caution, the term residential treatment center or RTC is related to state licensure. Each state defines RTC differently. An RTC in Utah, for example, may be licensed as a therapeutic boarding school in another state. Individual therapists are licensed to work as a mental health practitioner in the state the RTC is in. When I'm looking for a long-term residential placement for a client, I don't rely on the classification of the program as much as I do the needs of the client and where those needs can be met. There are some basic characteristics of residential treatment centers that I can help you understand, as well as who they serve and how they do the work they do.

Residential treatment centers are open 365 days a year. They do not close for holidays, weekends, or for any other reason. It is not unusual for students who have arrived in early December to spend Christmas at the residential treatment center. Residential treatment centers have psychiatrists on staff or have psychiatrists who contract with them. This is important because many of the children and teens who are in RTCs are on psychiatric medication; these medications need monitoring and often need to be tweaked.

Residential treatment centers have an academic component. They are accredited schools and can offer academic credits that transfer back to a child's home school. This can look different in different programs. Some RTCs do what is known as "packet work." Packet work is really what it sounds like: students are given packets to work on independently, at their own pace. there is a tutor or a teacher available to help them if they run into any difficulty. In other RTCs, schools look very much like a traditional classroom with a teacher at the front of the classroom teaching a lesson, and students taking notes, working on problems at their seat, and participating in discussion about the topic. Often at this level of care, academics do not take place for the entire day. Rather, part of the day is spent in school and the rest of the day is spent doing therapeutic work. Depending on the program, therapeutic work can be experiential, where students are out hiking, rock climbing, farming or fishing. It could be sitting in a group specific to an issue, such as adoption or substance abuse; it could be volunteering in the community alongside mental health workers from the program.

RTCs understand the connection between physical and mental health. Many have movement components (think yoga), exercise components (think training for a half marathon) and teach nutrition and mindfulness skills.

Often RTCs are small. It's not unusual for the whole program to have thirty-five students or less. A therapist's caseload should be small with no more than eight to ten clients. RTCs are often "boutique" type programs with a specialty in a specific issue, such as trauma, adoption, substance abuse, or autism. Many of the programs are built around a niche: a ranch where the kids participate in daily animal care, art programming where the arts are used therapeutically, and adventure activities where rock climbing, canyoneering and other outdoor activities are part of the therapeutic experience.

RTCs have a high level of supervision, often with a ratio of one staff member for every four students in the program. Participants meet with their individual therapist one to two times a week, participate in group every day, and have family sessions, usually via video once a week. Days are very structured, and students are required to wake up at a certain time, be out of bed at a certain time, take care of their hygiene and clean their rooms, all according to a schedule.

In some programs not following the rules will result in a loss of privileges. Compliance with expectations earns privileges. This is known as a *behavioral* approach. For some this may be effective. For others behavior changes aren't maintained when the carrots and sticks are removed. Some programs have a different philosophy and prefer to use what is known as a *relational* approach. Relational programs use the interactions between therapists and staff and the client to foster change in behavior and patterns. Using authentic interactions, the young person is guided to understand her usual way of relating and make healthy changes when necessary.

How often will I see my child?

Very often residential treatment centers want new students to spend time in their program on their campus before visiting with family. Time requirements vary from program to program, but after a few weeks to a month or two, you will be invited to spend time with your child on campus. The visit will be supervised by program staff, and there will be family therapy sessions. You will stay in a hotel at night while your child sleeps at the program. Family time becomes progressively less monitored and less prescribed. The next visit will typically be off campus, but nearby. By the time you and your child are off-campus, there have already been discussions about expectations around things such as meals, electronics, family time, and activities you will be doing.

Eventually your child will come home for visits. And again, there will be expectations set about how the time at home will be spent. The first two visits are designed to build family relationships at home. This means there will be limited, if any at all, visits with the child's friends. Eventually, visits will include time with friends in and out of the house so you and your child can practice more real-life situations. I have observed that parents who follow the rules have children who follow the rules. Conversely, if you decide an agreed upon rule isn't important, or is too difficult to enforce, your child will selectively adhere to the agreement too.

How will I communicate with my child?

Unlike wilderness programs, families can talk on the phone with their children. There are usually "social calls" (differentiated from family therapy calls) a few times a week. Often, they are monitored by program staff; there is no "true" privacy in residential treatment. Do not expect to be able to email your child. Many RTCs don't allow students to use electronics or have access to the internet.

How long do kids stay in RTC?

The answer varies from program to program and from family to family. However, a typical length of stay in an RTC is nine months to a year. Remember, this is the chance for your child to learn to swim in the middle of the pool with a lifeguard. Practice makes perfect.

How much does it cost?

Families need to be prepared to spend $10,000 to $16,000 a month for a residential treatment center. Health insurance may cover *some* of the cost of therapy. And in some cases, your school district may be required to pay for the educational portion of the RTC.

A Case Study: Elana

Elana was fifteen when her father called me in a panic. "Our therapist said I have to call you and get my daughter help tonight or she might die." Sometimes I drop everything and work with a family in a life-or-death situation like this. Elana was using heroin. She was involved in online gambling and owed a lot of people a lot of money. Her parents were terrified for Elana's life. We had a consultation over the phone. I gathered information about Elana and about the family. I was able to determine that she could safely go to a wilderness program as soon as the next day and begin her treatment. The ability to work quickly in crises and make lifesaving recommendations is part of the value of working with an EC.

Elana's wilderness experience went as expected. There was major discomfort due to withdrawing from opiates, but the staff monitored her and knew she was medically safe. She was resistant to the program at first, but became increasingly interested, involved, and even helpful. She learned about addiction, about strategies to use to stave off cravings and how to have appropriate relationships –– something she missed out on the last two years when she was so deeply involved in drugs. As she grew a trusting relationship with her therapist, Elana told her about being raped by a family member when she was nine. Her therapist was trained in trauma therapy and was able to start Elana on a path of healing. After eleven weeks, Elana discharged to a residential treatment program that specialized in teenage girls with substance abuse problems and sexual trauma.

In addition to having individual therapy, Elana and her family were assigned to a separate family therapist who helped the family come to terms with the sexual abuse. Elana's parents were encouraged to get their own therapist at home who could help them through their difficult feelings around the incident.

Elana continued her substance-abuse work, went to school in the same building where she slept, ate and did her therapy. After a few months, staff members took her and a few other students to support groups in the community so they could learn about resources they had available to help them stay drug free once they returned home.

Elana practiced the skills she learned in wilderness for a long time in residential treatment, for close to a year. Elena had a slow reentry back to her home through visits both short and extended. She met with a new therapist with whom she would be working when she returned home. She also went on interviews to private schools so she could get a fresh start at a new school and not return to her old public school. And when she went home, Elana's parents had the support of a parent coach to help them understand Elana's behaviors and maintain appropriate rules and boundaries. Elana worked with a student mentor who spent time with Elana in the community and was available to her for extra support. "I was really scared to go home, even though I was looking forward to it," Elana confided in me. "I was worried about making mistakes and having to go away again, and scared I would disappoint my parents if I couldn't keep up in my new school." And Elana did make mistakes, but with the help of their support system, the family was able to see Elena's behavior for what it was — normal, typical, teenage behavior. And not only was Elana able to keep up in her new school, she excelled. Elana graduated high school with honors and was accepted into just the right, medium-sized university where she majored in psychology and was very involved in the school's recovery community.

CHAPTER 7

Therapeutic Boarding Schools

Therapeutic boarding school (TBS) is considered a "lower level of care" than RTC. The focus is on academics with therapy. (RTC is the inverse: a focus on therapy with academics.) Many TBSs have breaks, similar to a traditional school calendar, although they all are year round and students are there for the summer. You can expect that there will be times when the campus is closed, and your student must come home and cannot stay on campus.

In many TBSs, there is access to electronics: usually, electronics use takes the form of a gradual re-entry back to technology in a way that teaches students appropriate use and how to present themselves in an appropriate manner on social media.

Students still have individual, group and family therapy, but the main focus is on academics in a fully accredited college preparatory (when appropriate) curriculum. TBSs try to mimic a more "normal" feel than residential treatment centers. Students have a typical school day with classes and free periods, after school clubs and sports, and down time so they learn to manage their unstructured time in healthy ways. TBS is where students practice the skills they learned in primary care.

If your child refuses to go to a TBS, then it's not the right fit. A student needs to be willing to attend. They don't have to be excited, or even happy about it, but they have to arrive at the TBS understanding they are expected to stay and to participate, at least at a basic level. There are therapeutic boarding schools that are designed specifically for certain types of behaviors and some them are more general. There are TBSs that are geared to launch a student into a rigorous college and others that prepare their students for vocational programs after high school, and everything in between. Often, due to school refusal and/or treatment, students are behind academically. Because of the year-round nature of TBS, they are able to help students catch up and receive the credits they lack.

Typical Weekday Schedule at a Therapeutic Boarding School:

7 a.m.	Wake up, morning routine, breakfast
8 a.m.	Advisory group, all school meeting
9 a.m. to 12 p.m.	Academic classes
12 to 1 p.m.	Lunch
1 to 3 p.m.	Academic classes
4 to 5:30 p.m.	Sports and clubs
5:30 to 6 p.m.	Free time
6 to 7 p.m.	Dinner
7 to 7:30 p.m.	Dorm meeting and group
7:30 to 9 p.m.	Study hall
9 to 9:45 p.m.	Free time
9:45 p.m.	Lights out

A minimal stay at therapeutic boarding school is about a year. Although some students stay longer, often a junior who doesn't want to start at a new school for their senior year may choose to graduate from their TBS. Less intense therapeutic work and lower staff to student ratios than RTC means TBS tuition is less. It can range from $8,000 on the low the end, to $12,000 on the high end.

Some therapeutic boarding schools require their students to attend a wilderness or similar program before enrolling. When the short-term program is finished, it is advised that the child go straight to their new school.

Not surprisingly, however, many of the families I work with want their children to come home after finishing wilderness and before starting TBS. They have fantasies of a cozy week catching up with friends and family, great meals at home and at favorite restaurants, board games with grandma and movies with friends. THIS NEVER GOES WELL. There is too much difference between the structure and support of wilderness and a week home. I have parents ask themselves whose needs are they serving by doing this? And usually the answer is their own. It will assuage their guilt about the longer-term program. Also, they think it will repair the damage of pre-wilderness by seeing their child home and doing well.

"We knew it wouldn't be a good idea to take Anna home after wilderness and before she started her new school, but we had no idea how quickly she would return to her old ways in just the few days we spent traveling and shopping for things for her dorm room," said Karen, who went to her daughter's wilderness graduation in Utah and then spent the weekend in a hotel with her before dropping her off a few hours away. "It was pretty shocking to see how quickly she regressed with us. And equally as shocking to see how she got with the program when she got to her new school."

As much as TBSs want to create a normalized environment, students are held accountable in ways they wouldn't be in a non-therapeutic school. For instance, students must attend all meals, students' whereabouts are always known and their use of electronics is limited and monitored as well.

Questions to Ask Therapeutic Programs:

1. What is the therapeutic approach of your program and your therapists?

2. Who is a typical child in the program?

3. Who don't you accept?

4. What's a typical day like for a new child?

5. What type of supervision does your program provide?

6. How do you decide when a child is ready to leave?

7. How much time is spent in individual therapy? Group? Family?

8. How much time do they spend in school?

9. Are you an accredited school? By which organization(s?)

10. What is your family program like?

11. How do we communicate with our child? With program staff?

12. How much does the program cost? What does that cover? What is extra (and how much?)

CHAPTER 8

Specialized Supportive Boarding Schools

There are times when a therapeutic, residential setting isn't the right move for a child. Perhaps they went to a wilderness program or another short-term residential program and the treatment recommendations were for them not to go home, but that they didn't need the restrictiveness of an RTC or TBS, nor did they need therapeutic intensity. Maybe they have already been to a therapeutic residential program and they no longer need that level of care, but there isn't an appropriate school at home for them. Or there isn't a need for short term intervention and the student can enroll straight from home. Some kids need more support than a family–any family–can provide.

Often my clients think that boarding schools are just for elite scholars or athletes. In fact, there is a whole world of highly specialized boarding schools designed to support students with specific educational needs. Yes, there are the hockey schools and the Ivy-feeders, but there are also many fine boarding schools that serve students who love farming or industrial arts, and schools for those who thrive in an alternative learning environment. This diverse world of small and alternative boarding schools includes private schools whose mission is to support students with ADHD, learning disabilities, and autism spectrum disorders. Most of all, they provide predictable communities for students who may be sensitive, quirky, socially awkward, or just wanting to do something different. These schools follow a traditional, ten-month school calendar and typically cost $60,000 to $65,000 with some schools charging additional fees for learning support.

A Case Study: Anna

When I met Anna in my office, I was struck by how articulate she was. She obviously was very bright, maybe even brilliant. She told me about her internship at a senator's office, and spoke with genuine enthusiasm about the debate team she loved being a part of, and the school jazz band she was in. Although she was involved with these clubs and activities, and even though she went to school every day, she told me she felt like a failure––that she would never become anything. She also confided in me her fears about what awaited her after high school: that she would have to settle for a job as a check-out girl at the grocery store, and not be able to attend college like her older brother and sister.

Anna's parents didn't understand what was going on. Anna had excelled in school when she was younger. She was student of the month in middle school. She loved her sleep-away camp and had so many friends. However, once high school started, Anna seemed to be less social and less involved with school. Her siblings had attended the same school and had done hours of homework each night. Anna told her parents she was doing her work in school. But her report card told a different story––she was failing almost every class because she didn't hand in assignments.

Worse, she had told a friend that she felt so awful that sometimes she wished she would die. Her friend told the school guidance counselor, who met with Anna and called her parents. As a result, Anna started seeing a therapist who suggested that she needed a break from the stress of school and the pressure of her parents' expectations. Instead of focusing on academics, the therapist felt that Anna should focus on her mental health and be given access to professionals who could tease out what brought on her feelings of profound pessimism and inadequacy.

Anna's parents hired me, and after a thorough assessment, I determined that she would benefit from a wilderness program for girls with seemingly sudden onset depression, where she could also receive a thorough psychological review and educational testing. Her wilderness therapist became curious as to why Anna was avoiding things that required reading––such as reading a recipe when it was her time to cook a meal for the group. "She was really engaged and genuinely wanted to feel better. She participated in groups, she encouraged other girls who were struggling. But when it came time to read for a therapeutic assignment or read a letter from her parents, Anna kept busy with other things. I started to realize she was avoiding it," said the therapist.

Once Anna had completed her testing, she was diagnosed with dyslexia. Feeling safe and knowing she wouldn't be judged, Anna spoke with her therapist and confided that she really couldn't read. She was able to decipher enough through context clues to get by, but she couldn't decode the words on the page. Instead, she looked at pictures when she was read-ing from a newspaper and tried to get the gist from reading what she could and listening to what people were talking about. Typically, children are diagnosed with dyslexia at a much younger age, but it's not uncommon for very bright students to hide their reading difficulties for years. This is known as *stealth dyslexia*. To everyone's surprise, Anna was reading at only a first-grade level.

Anna's parents were at a loss. Although they knew she had difficulty reading, they never realized how bad it was or how far behind she actually was. Anna and her family had dreamed of her attending college and being a fashion designer. But with only two more years of high school left and with so much catching up do to, was college even in Anna's future?

Anna was in luck. A boarding school specifically for bright high schoolers with dyslexia would provide her with an immersive experience with experts who knew how to teach her the way her brain learned and how to get her up to grade level before college.

Why did this make more sense than a therapeutic boarding school or a residential treatment center? Anna's self-hatred and feelings of depres-sion were centered on her feelings of inadequacy because she couldn't read. Once diagnosed correctly and given hope that she could learn to read and could catch up, maybe even surpass her peers, Anna was hopeful and eager. She didn't have maladaptive behaviors such as substance use, temper tan-trums or self-harm. She could go home for summers, long weekends and school breaks without concern that she would regress into old behaviors. At the learning disability boarding school, a therapist who had a private practice in town saw students on campus once a week. Anna was able to check in with her and continue her therapeutic work as an outpatient with the convenience of not having to leave campus.

A nontherapeutic boarding school can be therapeutic for the right student for various reasons.

1. Predictability: Boarding schools provide a predictable routine that is impossible to replicate at home. Children and teenagers, particularly those who have had issues, thrive on predictable routines. At boarding school, meals are served at a precise time each day, a delivery person

brings the mail at the same time every day, and there are established routines that do not deviate because of a parent's work schedule. Boarding schools are organized to ensure predictability.

2. High-Interest Activities: At boarding school, what happens after school is just as important as what happens in the classroom. Difficult kids tend to be less difficult when they are engaged in activities they really enjoy. School offerings often include activities such yoga, outdoor bread baking, video game designing, music lessons, go-karting, sports and more. In many schools, participation in sports or arts is mandatory, ensuring student are engaged for a large portion of the day in faculty-led, structured activities. This also enables students with social issues to have an adult helping them navigate the social scene during non-academic time. At the right school, a student who has academic difficulties but excels on the field spends a large part of the day happily engaged in activities in which he shines and succeeds.

3. Transitions: Parents and teachers of challenging kids note that activity changes (i.e., lunch to classroom, school to home, etc.) can be difficult. In boarding school, transitions are kept to a minimum because the campus and school community remain constant even though activities change. Students who may act out and refuse to go to school when at home have less trouble at boarding school because their dorm parent is likely to be a teacher and also a companion at the breakfast table.

4. School Culture: At the right school, positive peer pressure can do wonders to turn opposition into eager participation. Different boarding schools have different cultures: some promote strong work ethic and community service, some breed strong love of the outdoors, while others value intellectual pursuits above all else. The momentum of the school community pulls most outliers along and helps them get with the program.

5. Quality of Life: A short walk across the boarding school campus is a welcome change from the lengthy bus ride many students must take to their day schools. At home, therapy and tutoring take up a lot of after school time for students who need extra support. In boarding school, many of these sessions are integrated into the daily routine. While learning to whip up a great dessert, culinary students may be coached in appropriate peer interaction; running for dorm president becomes an activity a dorm parent guides a student through. Tutoring is embedded into the students' academic day at boarding school, and after school is now available for other non-academic pursuits. And parents, too, benefit because they are no longer schedulers, chauffeurs and activity directors. They can devote their attention to the other children in the family, to their jobs and to themselves.

6. Physical Activity: Exercise has been proven to ease symptoms of ADHD and help with dysregulated behaviors. Boarding schools encourage, and often require, daily rigorous physical activity. Proximity to outdoor recreation, as well as on-campus facilities such as rock walls, hockey rinks, fishing ponds and mountain bike trails, make it easier to raise a kid's heart rate at boarding school than at home.

7. Small Class Size: Class size in boarding school is intentionally small. In some schools there are as few as three or four students per class, allowing students with learning disabilities and/or slow processing speeds to get individualized attention and at a learning pace they can manage. Traditional boarding schools generally keep class size to twelve or less. Boarding schools insist that their students receive plenty of positive adult interaction; challenged students do not fall through the cracks.

8. Independence: Students who have struggled often need to rely on parents to get through their day. At boarding school, systems are in place that encourage students to

function more independently. Typically, a student with executive functioning limitations[6] will need a parent to make sure homework assignments get to school. In a boarding school situation, that same student would have books and assignments both in the school room and in the dorm. Relying on the school's internal system, rather than a parent's vigilance, ensures greater independence for the student. The move toward independence is a crucial developmental step that easily gets tossed aside in a busy family. At home, these kids become more and more dependent as they get older, rather than acquiring the independence they often gain at boarding school.

In addition to not having mandatory therapy, specialized and supportive boarding schools are much less restrictive about what students do with their free time than therapeutic schools. Most require mandatory study hall. In some schools, this means every student is in their room, off electronics and working on schoolwork with dorm parents available. In other schools, students report to the library or other public space with subject teachers available to them. In still other schools, both options are available, taking into account a student's ability to manage his assignments and time independently.

If not in class and with no school obligations, boarding students can be in their dorm rooms, on electronics. They can also go off campus and can spend time unsupervised with friends. Parents are free to come to campus and take students to dinner, meet them at a sports game and have them come home for a weekend.

A typical supportive boarding school schedule looks like this:

7:00 a.m.	Students responsible for waking up themselves
7:30 to 8:30 a.m.	Breakfast available in dining hall
8:45 to 9:00 a.m.	Advisor time. A small group meets with their advisor

---

6 Executive functioning limitations refer to difficulties with the organizing, initiating, executing and planning that's required to be successful in school and other areas of life.

9:00 a.m. to 3:30 p.m.	Academic classes, lunch time, and learning support periods
3:45 to 5:15 p.m.	Team practice and performing arts practice
5:15 to 6:00 p.m.	Free time
6:00 to 7:15 p.m.	Dinner
7:30 to 9:30 p.m.	Mandatory study hall
10:30 p.m.	Lights out and wifi is turned off

As you can see, there are multiple times throughout the day when adults are interacting with and checking on students. However, these schools aren't designed to provide the supervision or support that therapeutic schools can. It is very important to understand how the boarding schools you are considering supervise their students and what level of supervision they provide. Will they collect electronics at night, so kids are sleeping instead of gaming? Will they make sure students are eating meals in the dining hall?

Here are the top ten questions to ask supportive boarding schools when considering them for your child:

1. Is there an advisory system in place? How does it function?

2. What types of academic support are offered? What are the fees?

3. How does your school communicate with parents? How often?

4. How will the school respond if my child has trouble adjusting socially? Academically?

5. Is there a counselor on campus? Can my child see a therapist off campus? How about Skyping with their home therapist?

6. What are weekends like?

7. Are meals mandatory?

8. Are there rules around electronics and social media?

9. How much homework is typical per night?

10. What is study hall like?

CHAPTER 9

Young Adult Programs

While much of what has been written in this book holds true for struggling children, teens *and* young adults, there are some factors that are unique to treatment for a child over the age of eighteen. Here are some legal and practical considerations to keep in mind when dealing with a child who is eighteen or older.

Must Be Willing to Go: This doesn't mean your son or daughter has to be excited, or even happy, to enter a treatment program, but they must consent. It's a matter of law. In the United States, no one over the age of eighteen––unless someone has been granted decision making powers or guardianship over that individual––can be forced to attend a residential program against his or her will. The sole exception to the law pertains to acute inpatient hospitalization; the rules concerning keeping an adult in a psychiatric hospital against his or her will vary from state to state.

Program Age Restrictions: Many programs that accept teens cannot also accept someone over the age of eighteen, and in some cases, someone approaching the age of eighteen. When trying to find a program that is right for your son or daughter, it is important to ask about age restrictions when considering what options are available to you.

Parents Still Have Power: Although you cannot *force* your young adult to go to a treatment facility, you can still *insist*. Parents of this age group typically have the power of the purse. Do you pay for your young adult's tuition, cell phone, rent, groceries, car, car insurance, gas, spending money? When your young adult needs residential treatment and is unwilling to go, you can send a very clear message to them by withdrawing your financial support.

A Case Study: Lauren

"Lauren had already taken two medical leaves of absence from college and that was before the end of her freshman year!" recalled Stan, Lauren's father. "When I came to visit for Parent's Day and saw that she hadn't done laundry all semester, looked really disheveled and very thin, I realized that she was very likely dealing with an anorexia relapse." Lauren's physician confirmed her father's suspicion, and Lauren stayed home for the rest of the semester to attend an IOP for eating disorders.

Soon after Lauren returned to school, Stan got a call from his daughter's college. He was informed that Lauren had gone to counseling services, and that she had told her counselor that she was feeling suicidal. "They said they felt Lauren should take a medical leave and come back for the summer semester," Stan said. "But within two weeks of being home, Lauren was saying she could handle college. That it would be different this time. I knew she needed more help than meeting with a local therapist a few times a week. But if I would even mention it, she would completely blow up and then go into shutdown mode. Finally, I told her I would not pay for college until she successfully completed a residential treatment program. She even tried to get a loan so she could pay for school. Eventually she realized that without my financial support she wouldn't be able to go back. That's the carrot that got her in. She wanted to leave a few times, but I refused to pay for a plane ticket. With the help of her supportive therapist there, she stayed. And she really did well. She's even back at school finishing her junior year––with my blessing this time!"

Young Adult Transition Programs:

Young adults can still attend wilderness programs, stabilization and assessment programs, and short and long-term RTCs. In addition, there are programs called "transition programs" for young adults who are ready to "dip their toe" into school or the work world and learn how to live as an independent adult. These programs allow participants to live with people their age, often with similar struggles, and learn life skills such as budgeting, meal planning, cooking, wellness, etc. Transition programs provide programming and support to teach these skills. Depending on the program, they may also provide academic, vocational, social and therapeutic support.

You will find transition programs in rural areas, large cities and everywhere in between. While these programs have typically served young adults eighteen to twenty-one years old, the definition of "young adult" is expanding to include thirty-somethings.

Very often clients will move through a system of graduated supports, referred to as "stepping down" in care. Initially, a young adult will have a high level of supervision and structure in his daily life. Over time, the young adult becomes less accountable to program staff and more independent as he gradually takes on more responsibility. This progress is achieved in stages. The crucial issue of *when* the client is deemed ready to move on to the next stage and become more self-regulating is determined by all involved—the treatment team, the client's family and the client himself. Ultimately, he will step down to independent living with little or no support from the program. It's not unusual for young adults to decide to remain nearby once they have graduated from the program. Some transition programs provide outpatient services to their alums.

A Case Study: Oliver

Oliver graduated high school without much direction. He had applied, under considerable pressure from his parents and guidance counselor, to four colleges and was accepted at two of them. Which meant he had to make a decision. "With Oliver, no decision was a decision," explained his mother. "He wouldn't talk about college unless I brought it up. When it was time to commit to a school, he just simply never took that step. So, without a plan for the next year, my husband and I tried to get Oliver to design a 'gap year.' We were hoping with an extra year of maturity that he would eventually show some willingness to go on to college." Oliver and his parents, with the help of a therapist who had worked with the family on and off for a few years, put together a program for Oliver's "gap year."

"The plan was for Oliver to get a part-time job and have an internship working with a local jewelry designer since Oliver had shown an interest in jewelry making in summer camp," explained Oliver's mother.

But from day one, Oliver and his parents fought about him getting up in the morning, about staying out late at night, about calling in sick to his job—and sometimes he just didn't show up. "We were constantly arguing with him while all his friends were off at college doing what college kids are supposed to do," recalled Oliver's father.

After six weeks of struggling, everyone agreed that the gap year wasn't working. The family therapist suggested Oliver and his parents seek guidance from me about college alternatives. Alternatives that would "launch" him, either into a four-year school or maybe something less traditional. The therapist was also concerned that some of Oliver's apathy was stemming from depression.

My first meeting with Oliver included his parents, prior to he and I meeting alone. The first step I took with the family was to hear about Oliver when he was a little boy. Often parents bring up information the young adult doesn't remember. "He absolutely hated soccer when he was five. One of us would have to get on the field with him and hold his hand to get him to participate," his mom laughed. Parents, and sometimes Oliver, painted a picture of Oliver's childhood through high school graduation.

After gathering the history, I asked the parents to tell me what their goals for Oliver were—what they wanted him to achieve. They quickly came up with three vital goals for their son:

To find some direction. It doesn't have to be college, they said, but it has to be something that will prepare him to make a living, and hopefully something that he enjoys.

To be able to make decisions and not let life just happen to him, but instead be an active participant.

To live on his own.

Next, it was Oliver's turn to tell me what he wanted for himself. In typical Oliver fashion, he shrugged his shoulders and told me that what his parents had said was fine.

The second part of the meeting was just Oliver and me. We went on to discuss more sensitive topics, such as substance use and sexuality-- the things young people are often reluctant to talk about when parents are within earshot. Surprisingly, Oliver was much more talkative and open than he was when we all met together. He confided in me that he had dated a few boys in high school, but his parents didn't know he was gay. He also told me about his experience smoking marijuana, which had a pattern of increasing when big decisions needed to be made, such as choosing a college. I listened to what he had to say, then asked Oliver if he was prepared to be open minded and explore various options that I would come up with for him; he readily agreed.

When working with someone over eighteen, I explain to the family that the parents are my customers and the young person is my client. Nothing will be presented as an option without the parents first reviewing and agreeing it is an option that they are willing to finance. I also explained that the information Oliver and I discussed wouldn't be shared with his parents unless there was concern for his or someone else's safety.

Together over the next week, Oliver and I called two wilderness programs his parents had already vetted. Reluctantly, Oliver agreed to attend one of them. His wilderness therapist recommended that Oliver go to a young adult transition program after wilderness. "Oliver came to the woods with a long history of untreated depression," his wilderness therapist told me during our weekly call after Oliver had been there for four weeks. "After a few weeks there was a notable change in his mood. He was much more animated when he spoke, and he was an active participant in the things the groups did." Oliver really needed a structured environment with positive peers and good therapy to continue stabilizing his mood. He also needed some direction with his life.

Including Oliver in the discussion about aftercare was essential to success in the transition program, so I met with him in person at the wilderness program. He was much more engaged than when we met in my office. He spoke with a strong voice this time and looked healthy, albeit a little rough around the edges after living outside for a few weeks. We talked about what Oliver had learned and what he needed to do in order to sustain his newly found success. We also discussed what he *needed* – versus what he *wanted* – and that I would be taking both into account.

I used the information to identify three choices––all of which Oliver's parents felt were good options. Oliver's wilderness therapist provided him with information about the programs and arranged for Oliver to speak with the staff at the selected programs. With some coaching from his therapist, the wilderness staff and input from the other guys in his group, Oliver chose a transition program that suited him. He would live in a supervised residential setting––a house with other young adults and also with on-site staff available twenty-four hours a day, seven days a week. At the transition program, Oliver was assigned a therapist who met with him individually once a week. Oliver also had group therapy four times a week and family sessions once a week. When not engaged in therapy, Oliver worked with a life coach to schedule his routine of physical exercise, weekly meal planning, shopping and cooking and leisure activities. The coach also taught Oliver how to budget the money he was given for groceries, transportation and other essentials.

After a few weeks of working closely with his coach, Oliver accepted a position as an intern that required him to work ten hours a week; during his internship, he continued receiving support from his life coach. In Oliver's case, when the internship was over, he was asked to join the company as a part-time employee. Oliver petitioned his treatment team to allow him to move into a program apartment where he would pay rent and bills––again with oversight from his coach––and have more unsupervised time.

After a few months of successfully living in the apartment, Oliver was ready to enroll in a class at a nearby university, eventually taking nine credits and holding his part-time job. He then took another step forward by enrolling in college fulltime and moving into an apartment that he shared with a friend from the program. During this period of adjustment and transition, he continued to see his program therapist and also came to weekly community dinners at the program.

"It was a long haul, and definitely not the same path most kids take," reflected Oliver's mom. "But he did it. With a lot of intentional support, Oliver was able to feel good and get back on track with school and his life."

CHAPTER 10

Decision Time

How do you truly know which residential program is going to be best for your child and your family? Rely on your EC who has visited the programs she is suggesting. Discuss with your EC the important factors they used to create a program list specifically for your child. Be sure the discussion includes:

- *Type of Clinical Support:* This is the most important factor. Your child's therapeutic needs must be aligned with the program's ability to provide services that match those needs. Does your child have a substance abuse issue? Does the program address this by providing substance abuse groups, sobriety coaching, access to twelve-step meetings? If your child is adopted, is the program well versed in adoption issues? Whether the concern is trauma, an eating disorder, self-harm or mood dysregulation, the program must be well versed in whatever your child's maladaptive behaviors have been.

- *Delivery of Clinical Support:* How many hours of therapy will your child receive each week and in what format? Individual? Group? Family? Does the therapy style match how your child responds best? Some teens do well sitting in a traditional therapist's office and having a session. The room, the "formality" helps them focus and signals that it's "therapy time." For others, sitting still goes against their neurology; they need to move and talk. Is this your child? Does the program allow for flexibility in therapy style?

- *Academic Fit:* The programs I refer my clients to almost always have an academic component to them. (The exception is wilderness programs; most wilderness programs do not have formal academics.) It is important to understand the type of learner your child is. Even when there is no comprehensive academic component, participants are typically expected to complete therapeutic reading and writing assignments; if your child has difficulty with either, will the program find alternate ways for them to complete assignments? Does your child need learning support in the form of tutoring for specific subject matter? Help with organization and time management? Are they behind in their academic skills and need remediation help to catch up to their grade level? Do they learn best in a traditional classroom, or are they a more hands-on learner?

• *Social Fit:* You'll want your child to find his "tribe" whoever they may be. Maybe it's the skateboarding crowd, or the Dungeons & Dragons guys. Visiting, speaking with other parents, the program, and your EC--all help you understand the types of kids who attend the program and if your child will feel he fits in.

• *The Hook:* Programs have different areas of focus and specialization. Some specialize in the arts, some outdoor activities; there are programs with working farms, while others focus on sports. Often times, interests and recreational activities are the gateway to therapeutic work. Hanging out with a group of guys and staff fly fishing–with intention–can be a "sideways" way of doing therapy or learning new interpersonal skills.

"I found that when we were looking at programs for Sam, I had to constantly ask myself, 'Whose needs were my decisions serving?' I really liked the idea of him being around the quirky kids and being part of the robotics club, but I realized that wasn't really him. That is who I thought he was, and maybe who I wished he was, but he was better suited to be in a program with the sports crowd."

• *Trust:* When your child tells you everything is awful and they are being treated poorly, whom do you believe? Can you envision yourself trusting your child's therapist when he tells you that your child is tugging at your heart strings and in reality, he doesn't really lie in bed all day wasting your money? In the face of negotiations, tantrums and opposition from your child on a home visit, will you trust the program when you are told that bringing her back there is the right thing to do?

Ways to Develop Trust in Your Child's Residential Program

Establishing confidence in the suitability of a residential program—the people who work there, its methods, student community and how it feels to you—can be a vital step toward determining if a particular program is the right fit for your child.

Ask your educational consultant, "Why did you choose this place for my son?"

Speak with current and former parents. Ask what their experience has been like. What was surprising to them? Where do they feel the program's strengths lie? What have they been unhappy about?

Go visit the program. It's disruptive, it's expensive but it's necessary. Remember when you were in high school and you went on college visits? You knew it was the right one when you stepped on the campus. Visiting TBSs and RTCs is often similar; there's a "feeling" you get when you are at the right one for your child and family.

It's important to spend time with the students in the program. During your tour you may have a chance to speak with students without the staff. It's a chance to hear about their experiences in an authentic way.

I often give my families very different types of places from which to choose: one in a rural area where the kids are taking care of calves; one in a neighborhood where the kids are doing community service and going to the local gym; and a third that looks like a college campus. All three places have the therapeutic, academic and social support their child needs, but all go about it differently. Now the family needs to see what feels the most comfortable to them and what their connection is to the people at the program, including the other students.

How NOT to Make a Decision:

Too often, worried parents get sidetracked or even derailed by their fears and anxieties. At the top of the list is a preoccupation with the notion that any decision they make will end in hurt feelings and resentment on the part of their child.

"Sally will be so disappointed if she goes to a program."

"Sara loves field hockey. She will be crushed to have to give it up for her sophomore year."

"I promised Jason we wouldn't send him to a program that was far away."

"Daniel was really excited about our family vacation this year. I know his wilderness therapist and the TBS said he should go directly from one to another, but we don't want him to be upset about missing the trip."

Your child's job is to push back against the scary and unknown. Your job as a parent is to do it anyway.

Another pitfall awaiting anxious parents is a resistance to placing their child in a program that is not nearby. Very often, parents tell me their child *has* to be close by. There is comfort in knowing your child isn't too far away, but it doesn't mean you will see him more often. In residential programs there are restrictions on how often you can visit. Proximity doesn't dictate relationships. Having a child in a residential program where she is calm, introspective, and getting her needs met, means you will have a better relationship than if she were in a program that didn't meet her needs but was in driving distance to home.

Programs tend to be in areas of the country that limit the rights of children. In some states in the Northeast, for instance, anyone over the age of fourteen needs to give consent for mental health treatment, while in other states, an under eighteen-year-old is mandated to be in a program if his or her parent or guardian enrolls them. If you don't live near the right treatment facility for your child, and chances are you won't, you could be faced with the possibility of putting your son or daughter on a flight to a distant location. It won't be easy, but it is often the best decision you can make.

"The thought of my sixteen-year-old daughter being a plane ride away was almost too much for my wife and me to bear," said Rob. "This wasn't what we had ever planned. We thought if we could have her in treatment close to home it would be helpful. But we looked at two programs that were in driving distance, and then at other programs that were much further away, and we knew the answer. We didn't like the answer, but we knew it. She would have to go to the program that was the furthest away from us because it had the right mix of treatment and the right type of school for her. We only wanted to do this once, so we needed to get it right."

Online reviews can be misleading and unreliable. Don't be swayed by anonymous negative reviews on consumer websites such as Yelp and others. Base your decision on first-hand knowledge--information from your EC, other parents who have had children in the program and from your visit. You never know who has written online reviews. Imagine if your child left a treatment program early--what would they write about it? That's often whose negative reviews you are reading.

CHAPTER 11

How to Get Your Child to a Therapeutic Program

"I can't get him to go him to go to school. How on earth will I get him to go to wilderness?" This is a legitimate question asked by many parents. Their child is oppositional, scared, anxious, sad, depressed––everything but cooperative. If they can't get their child to fulfill basic expectations, how will they get him to fly across the country to participate in a program he doesn't want to go to? (And many of these programs are in rural areas that require a plane trip to access.)

When I tell parents the solution that works for all of these kids who won't willingly go, those parents are at best skeptical, and at worst horrified. But, after I explain, in detail, how transport companies work, and after I tell them about all the success stories I've witnessed, they understand and agree that this is, literally, the way to go. Just because it sounds scary, doesn't mean it isn't beneficial.

If safety and flight risk are not an issue, then you can consider traveling with your child to the treatment program you have selected. However, if you, who know your child best, believe that he or she will not willingly go, the solution is to hire a transport company to bring your child to treatment. Some parents do not feel strong enough to travel with their child without breaking down themselves. "I cried at the bus when she was going to sleepaway soccer camp," said a single mother in my office just a few months ago. "How will I manage leaving her at a wilderness program? I know I need to hire an experienced person to escort her there; they won't break down like I will."

There are times when it is unsafe to tell a child about the plan to send him to a treatment program. As stated earlier, some children will run away, or hurt themselves, or harm others when told they must leave their home. In these situations, parents consult with the transport company and arrangements are made carefully and thoughtfully. There are a handful of companies that provide transport services to take a child or teen to a therapeutic program. Every detail is discussed and rehearsed. The transporters do not use fear or intimidation. They are trained to be calm and compassionate with your child.

As prearranged, they come to the house very early in the morning--often at 2 a.m. or 3 a.m., while the child is asleep. It's not a good idea for siblings to be home; this is a time for them to be sleeping at their grandparents' house or the house of a friend.

Doing the intervention during the night means the teen is home and there won't be any friends around. In addition, leaving in the middle of the night helps with logistics. Many programs are a long flight away and admission staff prefer an early enrollment over a late one. This ensures a new wilderness participant joins their group while it is still light out. If transporters pick up later, it may mean transporters will have to stay in a hotel with the child. "That can cause more anxiety for parents than the early morning pickup," says Shepherd. "It also will raise the cost." When the scheduled time arrives for the child to leave, the parents go into his room, wake up the sleeping child and briefly tell him what is happening. "Dan, wake up. You know dad and I have been so worried about you. We are committed to getting you the help you need. We've hired Jack and Jill to take you to a great program we know is going to help our family. We love you."

The parents then leave the room and also the house, as planned. Next, the transporters talk with the child, build rapport, and keep him calm and focused on getting dressed, out the door and on his way. Kids usually respond by either verbally acting out or by becoming quiet and taking time to understand what's happening. Transporters plan to spend about an hour in the house. They explain what city they'll be going to and how they'll be getting there--via car and plane.

Without an audience, even the most oppositional kids get dressed and get on the road. A sense of slumbery confusion, often mixed with relief, motivates these kids to listen to the transporters who drive to the airport and travel with the teen. Once he gets into the car, the child finds snacks to eat and his favorite playlist piped through the car's speakers. The child will sit in the back seat with the primary interventionist, while the secondary person drives. Parents receive updates throughout the transport.

Many of the parents I work with worry their child will never trust them again, and that the child will feel betrayed. "True betrayal," says Brian Shepherd, president of Right Direction Crisis Intervention, a national transport company, "is knowing your child is struggling with serious problems, and you may have a solution, but you are unwilling to try that solution.

Please don't trick your child, don't lie to your child, and don't tell them far in advance-- even pleasant events get us nervous when we have too much lead time. And don't bribe them (e.g., "If you go, we'll buy you a car or puppy or Gucci watch.")

Often parents agree that being the ones to escort their child to the program is not a good idea. They realize this isn't an area where they can skimp or save. But they wonder if the transport company has to come in and surprise the child. Shepherd of Right Directions explains that it's important for a professional to do a risk assessment. "Parents need to have a conversation with the transport company to decide if the child should know ahead of time about the plans," says Shepherd. "There needs to be an assessment to determine if the child or teen is a run risk." Many relevant and important questions need to be asked and answered, he adds. "Is there a history of suicide attempts? What is the family dynamic like? Is there past trauma? When safety and flight risk are not an issue, we like to tell the kid," says Shepherd. All of this preparation helps ensure that the actual transport will go smoothly. **Studies show that transported kids do as well, if not better, than the kids who are taken to wilderness programs by family.**

Ten Questions to Ask When Considering a Transport/ Intervention Company

Once you have made the decision to use a transport company, it helps to know what questions to ask to choose the right one. Rely on a referral from your EC to be sure you are working with a reputable company. Another resource is The Association of Mediation and Transport Services. AMATS is an organization founded to regulate the standards of transport companies and is open to all organizations that meet the qualifying guidelines. They provide a list of ten questions for parents to consider when hiring a transport company:

Q: How long have you been in business?

Younger companies are not necessarily lesser companies, but this is a good starting point. It is also good to know the personal experience of the Director/Owner.

Q: How much and what type of professional insurance coverage does your company carry?

The industry standard is $1million. This is also the AMATS requirement. It's not a bad idea to ask for a copy of a company's proof of insurance binder with broker contact information. If a company or individual is not willing to invest in the correct professional insurance coverage for themselves and their clients, why would you want to entrust a loved one with them? This is probably the single biggest distinguishing factor between people and companies who are committed to providing a professional and lasting quality of service and those who are willing to cut corners.

Q: Are your transport agents employees of your company and not contracted?

AMATS requires its members to either employ their agents, so they are covered under the company insurance policy, or show proof the contractor has coverage that meets the $1 million minimum. This also reverts back to the previous question, because if the individuals working with your loved one do not fall under the insurance coverage, what's the point of having the insurance in the first place?

Q: What kind of background checks do you perform on your employees?

FBI biometric background checks are the standard for AMATS members, and the California Trustline Registry is required for companies working out of the state of California.

Q: Is your company independent of programs and schools in the special needs industry?

It is generally accepted in this industry that there may be a conflict of interest if the program your child is being taken to also owns the company doing the transport.

Q: What is your policy regarding physical restraints and mechanical restraints?

It's important for you to understand this policy and are comfortable with how this is implemented if ever necessary. This is something that very rarely happens.

Q: What is your policy regarding the training of your transport staff?

It is important the primary agent doing the transport has a high level of experience and training. It's a good idea to get an explanation of the company's specific training procedures.

Q: Do you always have at least one transporter who is of the same gender as my child?

This is not a rule or law, but rather it's just common sense and professionalism.

Q: Does your state require licensing of your business and if so, are you licensed?

Most states don't require specific licensing regarding the transporting of clients, but some do. A bare minimum should be that they are licensed to operate as a business so that you know they are accountable for their operation.

Conclusion

The *Leave It to Beaver* days are over. In the new millennium, our families are complicated. We've got stepchildren, half siblings, adopted siblings, IVF babies, egg donors, sperm donors, and surrogates. Kids are complicated. They are anxious, they are school refusing. They are obsessive compulsive. They are cutting. They are online. They are exposed to so much.

But there's hope. Families who are willing to be vulnerable and open their homes and their hearts can heal. Their children get better. You, too, can heal, and your children can get better. You can move beyond the crises and the difficult times and reach that light at the end of the tunnel. If you've read this book, it's because you can't do it alone. You need a professional to guide you and your child through a healing process. An educational consultant is that professional, fresh set of eyes who will look at your child's issues and lead you through the overwhelming world of residential treatment. This a confusing and confounding task, but I deal with it every day. You are not alone.

Read through the case studies presented in this book. Do you see yourself, your family and child reflected in these stories? Every situation is nuanced, but there are common threads:

- Outpatient therapy, medication, hospitalizations aren't helping.
- Consequences, alternative schooling haven't helped.
- You walk on eggshells, avoiding conflicts and meltdowns.
- Your child's functioning is impaired; your family's functioning is impaired.
- The police have been involved.
- Your child has been in a psychiatric hospital.
- No one--not therapists, teachers or doctors--have helpful answers.

If this sounds like your situation, call an educational consultant. It is the vital first step. Get fresh eyes on the problem. Then be prepared to ask more questions, do your homework, and be willing to make some difficult decisions, including not just where your child is going, but how to get her there. Expect a journey of more than one step and more than one stop along the way. All your difficult work is not only necessary, but I know from the hundreds of families I have worked with, that the difficult work is life changing and incredibly worthwhile.

What is an Assessment and Why Your Child Should Have One

Dr. Jennifer Zeisz

Dr. Jennifer Zeisz is a licensed clinical psychologist who earned her Ph.D. in clinical psychology from DePaul University in 1997. After completing her post-doctoral training at the Child Study Center in Chicago, she started her private practice in Asheville, North Carolina in 2001. Dr. Zeisz has more than twenty years of experience working with children, adolescents, young adults, and families. Today she travels nationwide conducting diagnostic, educational, and neurodevelopmental assessments in private settings, residential centers, and therapeutic wilderness programs. Her areas of expertise include developmental trauma, adoption, autism spectrum disorders, ADHD, learning differences, and mood/anxiety disorders. Dr. Zeisz approaches assessment in a therapeutic way; she conceptualizes her clients in a holistic manner and provides psychoeducation aimed at increasing understanding and compassion. In her free time, she enjoys cycling, kayaking, and hiking with her beloved dogs Ruby and Lily in the beautiful mountains of Western North Carolina.

Diagnosing children and adolescents can be challenging for a number of reasons. Often, they do not demonstrate the same symptoms as adults, or they may not be able to describe their symptoms. Their issues are further complicated by the fact that individuals develop and mature at varying rates. This makes it harder to assess whether a particular behavior is part of the maturing process or a sign of a deeper, ongoing problem. While it's not unusual for behavior problems to arise as part of normal development, there are some behaviors that are red flags--signs that something is not right. Temper tantrums that are normal for a toddler, for instance, are a cause for concern in a twelve-year-old.

One of the most important tools used to diagnosis your child and to understand his or her cognitive, educational, social, emotional, behavioral and intervention needs is *neuropsychological testing*. This type of testing is administered either by a psychologist or a neuropsychologist--a psychologist with special training in how an individual's brain processes information and how that impacts one's behavior and ability to learn. Your child will meet alone with the psychologist or neuropsychologist and engage in a variety of tasks that measure his strengths and weaknesses in different areas. Those include attention, memory, intelligence academic performance. A comprehensive neuropsychological evaluation should also include a social-emotional-behavioral profile. Typically, the testing is conducted for a few hours at a time over the course of several days. Once completed, you will receive a report detailing the results of the testing and also recommendations for addressing academic, social and emotional concerns.

The evaluation is key to guiding you and your EC to the appropriate treatment for your child. Consider it a blueprint or road map of your child's brain including the way she experiences and processes social-emotional experiences. By relying on data-based insight into how your child functions across important areas of life, the clinician can recommend the most effective ways to treat behavioral and emotional problems. Neuropsychological testing will also uncover learning disabilities, attention deficits, and processing issues that can affect your child both in and out of the classroom.

* * *

Parents who come to me seeking a diagnosis for their child are dealing with complex and persistent problems that aren't improving. Most struggle with the sense that the experts they have turned to for help have been unable to pin down what is wrong or tell them what can be done to help their son or daughter. Not surprisingly, these same parents feel that there are important pieces missing from the larger diagnostic puzzle–– often despite the long list of tests that have been conducted usually in a piecemeal manner.

An accurate diagnosis can shed a great deal of light on the child's behaviors at home, school and with peers. It can also inform the treatments and interventions that will be the most successful. A correct or accurate diagnosis—as opposed to an inaccurate one—changes the lens through which the child is viewed by her parents, teachers, professionals and even peers. This singular change in how the child is seen by others and the treatments and interventions used to help them can be genuinely transformative.

I will never forget working with a twelve-year-old girl who had been diagnosed with many serious disorders: conduct disorder, intermittent explosive disorder and a personality disorder! She was perceived as an "emotionally reactive," "stubborn," and "difficult" child who was "resistant" to therapy. A thorough developmental history along with formal testing and astute observations revealed that she was on the autism spectrum and had significant problems with social perception and sensory integration. Instead of continuing a regimen of behavioral interventions that had never worked, she received occupational therapy focused on helping her integrate her sensory experiences. She also received animal-assisted therapy to build social skills, and neurofeedback to help her brain develop new neural pathways to regulate her emotions. She went from being viewed as an incorrigible child to a young lady who was accurately perceived as capable of forming meaningful relationships, participating in family life, excelling at school, and demonstrating her gifts as an artist.

Who Should Receive an Assessment?

How do you know if your daughter or son is a candidate for an assessment? A comprehensive assessment is beneficial for a child or adolescent who demonstrates any of the following traits and behaviors.

1. **Developmental delay**: he or she does not seem to be meeting age-appropriate milestones, is displaying unusual or unexpected behaviors or seems different than her peers.

2. **Difficult temperament**: the child is inflexible, hard to soothe or has difficulty following basic rules and expectations; he holds the family hostage to demands and tantrums while being "perfect" outside of the home or at school.

3. **Poor academic performance or learning problems**: the student is not performing up to potential, dislikes or refuses school, seems discouraged or is a "class clown."

4. **Social problems**: the child is excessively naive or vulnerable to peer pressure, lacks empathy, does not

understand where others are coming from, has few if any friends or is rejected or bullied by peers.

5. **Anxiety or depression**: the child suffers from nervousness, sadness, isolation, lack of interest, expressions of low self-worth or feelings that others would be better off without them.

6. **Excessive gaming and screen time**: the child exhibits an inability to respect reasonable rules and limits, becomes emotionally dysregulated when on social media.

7. **Substance use**: the child resorts to use of alcohol, marijuana, cigarettes, vaping, illicit drugs, and prescription drugs.

8. **Excessively low self-esteem:** the child struggles with body image distortions, eating problems or identity and gender confusion, and/or has little confidence in his own worth and abilities.

9. **Nothing has worked**: the child is not responding to normal parenting; his problems are escalating, and parents are at the end of their rope.

Who Should Conduct the Assessment?

Once it has been determined that an assessment is appropriate, the next step is finding a qualified psychologist. Begin by talking with your child's educational consultant. She will often be able to recommend a qualified clinician. You can also often get referrals from your child's therapist or pediatrician.

Do your homework. Check to be sure that the clinician is fully qualified. It's important that whoever is conducting the assessment is a professional who holds a doctorate—signified by a Ph.D. or Psy.D. after their names. Master's level clinicians are qualified to do therapy and some types of assessments. However, they do not have the licensure to perform comprehensive psychological testing. The psychologist you choose should:

•

- specialize in testing and assessment with children and adolescents
- perform assessments on a regular basis
- use up-to-date tests and measures.

Ask about the clinician's experience in assessing for specific issues you feel may be relevant to your child, such as autism spectrum disorder or a specific learning issue. Lastly, ask for a "sanitized" report—one in which all identifying information has been removed—so you can review an actual report and get a sense of the clinician's work before committing to work together.

Where Are Assessments Performed?

Psychologists in private practice will typically perform the assessment in their office over several weeks. Others provide services on location at residential treatment centers, therapeutic schools, and therapeutic wilderness programs. And some will conduct evaluations at the child's home, school or other settings.

When the testing is complete, you will receive a written report with the testing results. There will be a reference to "the DSM," or the Diagnostic and Statistical Manual of Mental Disorders. The DSM was introduced in 1952, but has been modified several times over the years to reflect greater understanding of mental health problems. The DSM-5, the most recent edition, is designed to provide a research-based way for professionals to categorize a wide range of mental health problems and to communicate using a common language. The DSM-5 is not a perfect tool, and it is not unusual for an individual to meet some but not all of the criteria for a disorder. It is imperative that whoever is working with your child also understand the complexities of child and adolescent mental and behavioral health problems.

Preparing for an Assessment

Prior to testing, parents often voice concerns that the child or adolescent will not "show" their behaviors within the clinical setting. However, I have found that a child is likely to cooperate and perform quite well when she receives individualized attention from a psychologist who relates well to children and adolescents. It is important to stress that a psychologist's grasp of your child's functioning is also dependent on the ability of the parent or primary caregiver to provide reliable information. That means keeping careful records of your child's behaviors. Be sure to keep track of how the child's behaviors increase or change once the child begins taking medication. It is also important to ensure that the psychologist evaluating your child take a comprehensive developmental history, including infant temperament and childhood developmental milestones.

Timeframe and Setting for Conducting an Assessment

The amount of time needed to conduct a comprehensive evaluation and to produce a written report varies widely, depending on the psychologist, setting, and urgency. In an outpatient setting, an evaluation may take place in one-hour segments over a period of several weeks at the psychologist's office. The amount of time for a written report to be produced is highly variable, ranging from weeks to months. You should ask the clinician when you can expect to receive the finalized report.

In a residential treatment center, therapeutic school or therapeutic wilderness program, the psychologist may interview the parents and others in advance of the face-to-face testing session to gather historical information. Likewise, the clinician may ask the child to complete age appropriate questionnaires and ask the parents and teachers to also complete questionnaires and provide relevant information. The individual assessment session may be conducted at the school, program or in the field if the young person is in a wilderness program. The clinician will then spend anywhere from three to six hours with the child to get to know them, administer the tests, and to conduct an interview. Typically, in these settings, clinicians understand that time is of the essence, and reports are usually produced within ten to fourteen days.

The Completed Comprehensive Report

The written evaluation and report will typically contain the following specific information under these categories:

Developmental History: Prenatal and perinatal period, including prenatal exposure to neurotoxins; infant temperament, social reciprocity, and bonding; early childhood developmental milestones. Screening for unusual behaviors, "red flags" or early signs of an autism spectrum disorder. Screening for developmental trauma, including history of foster placement, institutionalized care, transitions and other potential disruptions to typical development. Sensory processing and integration.

Family Mental Health History: The person conducting the assessment will ask you about any mental health issues relatives have had on both sides of the family, usually immediate and extended family.

The Child's Mental and Physical Health History: You will be asked questions about your child's mental health issues throughout her lifetime. Be prepared to also tell the tester about any physical issues throughout your child's life, including major illnesses, concussions, accidents and surgeries.

Cognitive Functioning: Intellectual abilities and executive functions.

Academic Functioning: The grade level your child is achieving in school subjects. This includes engagement in school, classroom behaviors, learning issues and academic performance, and strengths and weaknesses.

Social and Emotional Functioning: Temperament, signs and symptoms of anxiety, depression, or other problems. Emotional and behavioral regulation, social skills, family and peer relationships and risky behaviors.

Summary and Diagnostic Impression: This section of the report will give an overview of your child's history, reasons for testing and what the testing results reveal.

Recommendations for Academics, Therapy, and Placement: The clinician has gathered information and made a diagnosis. This section is where she will explain what supports are needed, including accommodations in and out of the classroom and where your child's level of care falls on the continuum of treatment options.

Feedback Session: After the report is finalized and shared, there is much to discuss and explain. Hence the need for a feedback session with parents and others who will be part of the child's treatment plan. The clinician will arrange an in-person or remote meeting to answer questions and concerns and discuss results.

Common Issues and Diagnoses in Childhood and Adolescence

An important aspect of seeking an assessment is becoming educated about possible disabilities and disorders that may be at the root of the problems your child is experiencing. It therefore helps to be familiar with terms used to identify and describe various learning and behavioral problems, as well how these conditions are manifested and their effects.

1. Cognitive or Intellectual Delays: Children with global intellectual disabilities may learn information and concepts at a slower pace, appear socially immature, and require more repetition and support to perform tasks of daily living. Children with relatively strong verbal skills may "present well" and cognitive delays and learning differences may not be discovered until they struggle at school or demonstrate behavior problems.

2. Learning Disabilities: Learning disabilities (sometimes referred to learning disorders) are diagnosed when the child demonstrates significant struggles in a particular area, such as reading, writing or arithmetic. Learning disorders can overlap, and often co-occur in children with ADHD. Learning difficulties can be subtle and difficult to detect, so it's important to seek a professional assessment. Many children struggle through school for years without the appropriate interventions or accommodations. Although sometimes a child's school psychologist will perform an educational evaluation to determine if the child is eligible for special education services, these evaluations are typically not diagnostic. As a result, they may not take into account the impact of emotional, social, and behavioral issues on academic performance or functioning in other settings.

3. Autism Spectrum Disorders (ASD). The DSM-5 diagnostic label of ASD now encompasses what used to be termed "Asperger's Disorder" and "High Functioning Autism." Autism spectrum disorder is currently diagnosed using rating scales that express the severity

of restricted interests and social communication deficits to capture the wide range of presentations on the ASD continuum. The Centers for Disease Control estimates that one in fifty-nine children are diagnosed with an autism spectrum disorder and that boys are still about four times more likely to be diagnosed. Children as young as two years of age can be reliably diagnosed but most children are not diagnosed until after the age of four. In my experience, the struggles of children with ASD are frequently dismissed or misunderstood, leading to incorrect diagnoses, inappropriate treatments, and distressed families. If you are concerned that your child may be on the autism spectrum, follow your intuition and do not be deterred by those who say your child is "not like" children they know with ASD. Girls with ASD often present differently than boys, so it is imperative that the examiner is skilled in discerning the subtleties of female ASD.

4. Attention Deficit Hyperactivity Disorder (ADHD): It is estimated that anywhere from 5 to 11 percent of children and adolescents have been diagnosed with ADHD at some time. Girls may be underdiagnosed because they do not tend to engage in as many acting-out behaviors. Surface symptoms of ADHD are relatively easy to observe and understand: the child is off task, easily distracted, hyperactive, or impulsive. Underlying ADHD are the executive functions that can be thought as the command and control center of the brain. Those with ADHD, ASD and other difficulties often demonstrate significant deficits in their executive functions. (Problems with the EFs do not constitute a separate diagnosis but are discussed below for clarity.)

5. Parents often tell me that ADHD medications help their child's attention and hyperactivity, but they are confused as to why the child is still struggling in

school. Underlying the overt symptoms of ADHD that respond to medication, are the executive functions that include about fifty different metacognitive processes. Metacognitive processes, such as impulse control, planning, organization, sequencing, initiation, perseverance, and time management are the hidden keys to academic success, emotional regulation and social relationships. Children with ADHD, autism spectrum disorder and other issues almost always have underlying executive function deficits that contribute to discouragement, low self-esteem, behavior problems, homework battles, and disengagement from academics.

6. Oppositional Defiant Disorder (ODD): ODD includes negative or hostile attitudes towards authority, temper problems, and defiant, argumentative behaviors that may be particularly evident when rules are enforced. It is estimated that 50 percent of children with ADHD engage in disruptive behaviors, including blaming others and being easily angered. It is important that the examiner discern the underlying cause or root of the child's misbehavior. These problems can be driven by neurodevelopmental deficits and other factors that contribute to difficulty with self-direction and emotional or behavioral control. Children who struggle to inhibit their first impulse are likely to demonstrate a pattern of misbehavior, such as lying as a quick way to dismiss or deny the situation, and anger when held accountable for the original behavior. Many children labeled with ODD do not intentionally engage in these behaviors and their problems can be more accurately understood in other ways.

7. Conduct Disorder (CD): CD includes aggression, destruction of property, deceitfulness or theft, and serious rule violations. This is a serious diagnosis and it is important to keep in mind that many children and

adolescents will show a few of these behaviors at some point. Also, children who experienced trauma, abuse, neglect and institutionalized care (e.g., orphanages in Russia or China) may demonstrate these surface symptoms that are indicators of underlying trauma.

8. Prenatal Exposure: In the United States, there has been a steady increase in the number of infants born prenatally exposed to alcohol, illicit drugs, and opioids. Children adopted from Russia, China and other places have high rates of prenatal exposure to substances as well as environmental toxins. Discerning exactly which substance a baby was exposed to or determining the exact impact of the different substances is complicated. It is important to inform the examiner if prenatal exposure is suspected.

9. Developmental Trauma and Attachment Problems: The term developmental trauma includes but is not limited to the following: prenatal trauma, relinquishment, adoption, inadequate early caregiving, loss of parents, and life-altering transitions. These experiences can have a significant impact on the ability of the child to attach to others and to feel safe and secure in their relationships. Traumatic experiences are even more prevalent in children who have been placed in substitute care or who have experienced institutionalized care. These early experiences can have a profound impact on the child's brain development, attachment, self-soothing, and emotional regulation. Some children with early trauma will demonstrate attachment problems and some will exhibit severe symptoms associated with Reactive Attachment Disorder.

10. Anxiety: Approximately 4 percent of children present with subtle to severe forms of anxiety that can begin early in life. Symptoms may range from shyness to fearfulness to separation anxiety, where the child cannot tolerate being away from primary caregivers.

Anxiety often masquerades as a number of different behaviors, including irritability, refusal, defiance, and temper tantrums. Anxiety runs in families and children who have had adverse or traumatic experiences are even more likely to suffer from anxiety.

11. Depression: Approximately 3 percent of children suffer from depression. Symptoms include but are not limited to sadness, loss of interest, low self-worth, lack of energy and thoughts of death or suicidal ideation. Like anxiety, depression can have a genetic component. Depression places a child or adolescent at risk for isolation, substance use and other negative behaviors.

12. Bipolar: Occasionally a child or adolescent will present with symptoms that reflect an emerging bipolar mood disorder where periods of depression are punctuated by episodes of manic behaviors. This diagnosis requires a thorough developmental and family history and careful tracking of symptoms over time. The vast majority of children I see do not meet criteria for a bipolar mood disorder. I have seen far too many cases where children are hastily diagnosed and medicated for the wrong disorder with disastrous results.

13. Emotional and Behavioral Dysregulation: Many children present with what is more accurately characterized as emotional dysregulation. I often hear, "All of a sudden he melts down and has a temper tantrum for no reason." These children demonstrate emotional and behavioral dysregulation associated with other neurodevelopmental factors, including anxiety, weak executive functions, and sensory processing deficits that contribute to chronic nervous system "overload." Children with developmental trauma also struggle to regulate themselves. The clinician should strive to find the root causes of behavior.

14. Personality Disorders: Children and adolescents are sometimes diagnosed with personality disorders. A personality disorder is a chronic and pervasive way of responding to the world that is maladaptive. In my opinion, if a child has been given a personality disorder diagnosis it is highly likely that there is something else that is driving the child's behaviors. Sometimes one symptom, such as self-harm, is used to diagnose a personality disorder such as "borderline." Even at age sixteen or eighteen, these diagnoses should only be considered after everything else has been ruled-out. Be wary if your child or adolescent is diagnosed with a personality disorder and seek another opinion!

15. Gaming and Screen Addictions: It is important to note that children and adolescents with an ADHD profile are particularly drawn to electronics with a screen. This is because video games, television, or computers offer the brain a very high level of stimulation and sensory input but do not demand independent executive functioning and mental control. Gaming and other screen activities are characterized by rapid response, immediate reward, and multiple windows with different activities that reduce feelings of boredom. Problems with self control and shifting attention make it even more challenging for the child or adolescent to stop and transition to another activity, thus contributing to refusal or emotional dysregulation. (This inability to stop and move on is especially pronounced when the activity centers around screen time). At this time, there is no specific diagnosis to capture this increasingly common phenomenon. (Internet Gaming Disorder is proposed in the DSM-V as a condition for further study).

16. Pornography Addictions: With ready access to the internet, pornography addictions have become increasingly problematic in our children and adolescents. Behavioral addictions are described by

a loss of control, impairment, and risky use. Online pornography use is also on the rise, with a potential for addiction, considering the so-called triple A influence: accessibility, affordability and anonymity. This problematic use might have adverse effects in sexual development and sexual functioning, especially among the young population.

17. Self-harm Behavior: Self-harm can range from mild scratching of the skin with a fingernail to making superficial or deep cuts with sharp objects or tools-- often referred to as cutting. Self-harm behaviors can also include burning or severe picking of the skin. Self-harm behavior can take on an addictive quality as it provides temporary relief from emotional pain that overwhelms the adolescent's coping resources. Research indicates that cutting has become more frequent among adolescents in the general population. If your child or adolescent is engaging in self-harm, take action. This may be a sign of significant underlying emotional distress.

18. Substance Use: Current estimates indicate that 17 percent of high schoolers have used alcohol, prescription medications or other illicit drugs during school, with marijuana being the most widely used substance. Vaping has also become increasingly popular. Childhood and adolescent substance use contribute to a range of associated problems, including addictions, association with negative peers, behavior problems, poor academic performance, and a number of other risk factors. Substance abuse can be a sign of underlying problems such as low self-esteem, trauma, anxiety or depression.

Lists of Tests and Scales

It is helpful to be aware of the names and purpose of commonly used tests and scales likely to be administered during a comprehensive evaluation. (Keep in mind that there are many different tests and measures and this list provides examples but is by no means exhaustive.)

Intellectual Functioning and Intelligence: Wechsler Intelligence Scale for Children-V, Wechsler Adult Intelligence Scale-IV or similar.

Achievement Testing: Wechsler Achievement Test-II, Woodcock Johnson IV Tests of Achievement or similar. Additional tests are used if specific learning disorders in reading, math or writing are suspected.

Neuropsychological Screening: D-KEFS, NEPSY, Beery VMI, as well as tests assessing working memory and processing speed.

ADHD and Executive Functioning: Conners Parent and Teacher Rating Scales, Comprehensive Executive Function Inventory, Behavior Rating Inventory of Executive Function, Brown ADD Scales.

Autism Spectrum Disorder: Autism Spectrum Rating Scale, Social Responsiveness Scale, Social Communication Questionnaire, Sensory Profile. The ADOS-2 is a standardized assessment administered to the child by the clinician. It looks for social and communication behaviors and consists of games, books, pretend play, and conversation. Although some consider this tool the gold standard, children, particularly girls, who are high functioning may perform well on this test resulting in a false negative. As with any issue, be wary if a clinician bases his diagnosis on only one test or measure or has not taken a thorough developmental history.

Anxiety, Depression and Emotional Dysregulation: Behavior Assessment System for Children, Beck Youth Inventories, Revised Children's Anxiety and Depression Scale, Resiliency Scale for Children and Adolescents, Childhood Trauma Questionnaire, Child PTSD Symptom Scale.

Adaptive Functioning: Vineland-3, Adaptive Behavior Rating Scale (ABAS), Child Behavior Checklist, Achenbach System of Empirically Based Assessment, Sensory Profile.

Personality: Millon Pre-Adolescent Inventory, Millon Adolescent Inventory, Minnesota Multiphasic Personality Inventory-Adolescent.

Words of Wisdom

I'm so fortunate to maintain relationships with many of the families I've worked with, years after placing their child. I get emails letting me know Jane had a successful senior year at home and is now an excellent college student. Like we knew she could but were terrified she wouldn't. The quick pictures texted to my phone of Andrew performing a piano concerto on parents' weekend at his boarding school where he is excelling. Like we knew he could but were terrified he wouldn't. And the phone calls from an exuberant dad letting me know Dan is now a pilot, living his dream. Like we knew he could but were terrified he wouldn't.

These veteran parents have words of wisdom to share with you who are just starting this long journey.

* * *

My son and our family struggled for years. We volleyed back and forth between he was the problem and we were the problem. The reality is all kids are different and we needed to realize what worked for child number one may not work for child number two or three.

I truly wish I realized a few things earlier in my parenting years:

- *Good parents will still have children who struggle.*
- *My success as a parent is tied to my ability to give 100% of my effort, it is not measured by my child's success.*
- *Trusting my mother instinct trumps everything else.*
- *Only a parent who deeply and truly loves their children to the end of time would ever consider sending their child away to get help — we are brave and amazing parents.*
- *You get what you pay for, pick the best program for your child, regardless of its location and price.*
- *Be prepared to put your own work in; your child is not the only one in crisis, the entire family is.*
- *Never give up on your child or yourself.*
- *Find a community of parents in the same situation, they will understand you, support you, and will not judge you.*

- *This road has no timeline, do not restrict progress or success by a self-imposed timeline.*

Parent of a 16-year-old boy

(*The author of these words, Cheryl Mignone, invites you to visit her blog about her family's journey: "Letters to My Son" https://the-parent-support-network.com*)

* * *

As a parent who thought I could figure everything out on my own, I was beginning to see (after six rehabs/sober living facilities) that I needed help finding a possible solution. After more than three years of trying to navigate the insanely confusing world of endless internet searches, trying to find a place that could help my son, I started to feel that there was no place on this earth that could help him (he has many co-occurring issues- ASD, ADHD, depression, anxiety, in addition to addiction). I was terrified, as my son's bottoms were now flirting with death. I felt powerless, frozen with fear, and drained to the point of not knowing what to do next. When I reached out to Lucy, telling her I truly believed there was no place in existence that could help my son, she said, "There are! I can help you." Of course, I was skeptical, as I thought I had tried everything, but Lucy knew what I did not...that there WAS a place that could help my son, that there IS still hope, and that there has been great success with young adults like my son. Everything changed in that moment.

What I wish I had known early on, is that you don't have to do this on your own, that there is help out there, even if you think you have exhausted all options. ASK FOR HELP!

Parent of a 24-year-old man

* * *

This is the hardest, scariest, most nonmaternal decision you will make. The worst part is being in the in-between. You need to listen down deep to the part guiding you to what your child needs and separate that from the fear voices. But the truth is, nothing I will say will truly resonate until you live it and get to the other side. It is going to hurt like nothing else.

Parent of a 9-year-old boy

* * *

The most important thing I wish I knew before sending our daughter to wilderness and then therapeutic boarding school was that it wasn't only her that needed help — this is not a vacation from your kid — this is learning how to communicate, and the work never ends.

We learned fast but you need to go all in— take advantage of the weekly family counseling and if the program doesn't have it— find one that does. It is invaluable.

Also, know that those first letters home may be full of venom. It's understandable. When someone is sitting with themselves with no phone or computer and in the elements in nature, but with complete support from the group they discover things about themselves they never thought possible.

Parent of a 17-year-old girl

* * *

What would have been helpful for me to know before placing my son? Well anything that Lucy told me, I was going to do. That said, here are some of my thoughts:

Pick an EC that you trust and go with them.

Sending your child off to wilderness is especially difficult since you are not able to see them or talk with them.

Touch base with parents who have children that attend/ed the programs. You hear lots of stories out there. Talking with other parents, who have experience with a program you are considering, will calm your nerves, considerably.

You need to live in the moment. Your child will be a different person as they heal and move forward. When the time is right, you can start thinking of "what's next." You need to wait, as hard as that is, to see who your child is as they progress before you can consider the next placement.

It's OK to feel relief when your child is in wilderness or a boarding school. The family at home needs to heal from their experiences, too.

I felt sending my child to wilderness was a leap of faith. I have since learned that it was the ONLY choice. He needed to go, and I needed to be strong enough to let him.

Sending your child to wilderness or TBS is not a punishment. You are giving them an amazing gift, the gift of health and the possibility of a bright future.

You MUST be part of the process. There will be notes you need to write and things to say that will not be easy to do. It's part of the process. You need to have faith in the program you are sending your child to.

Parent of a 12-year-old boy

(Neala Schuster, the author of this advice, welcomes you to visit her blog to learn more about her family's story: Parentingmytransgenderchild. com)

* * *

My son was 13 years old when I first called the cops on him for help - a mother's nightmare. I felt so alone yet I knew we could not meet his needs. He was suffering so much. I wish the state counseling services we were receiving, or the school, my parent support group, or the ER — anyone during those months of crisis— would have said - you need an educational consultant, you don't have to send your child to a temporary IOP. Thankfully I fought - pulled him out of all the systems to attend a three-month therapeutic residential treatment center - which established a trajectory for us to learn about consultants and obtain a higher level of care he continues to need at sixteen.

Parent of a 16-year-old boy